FIT TO SERVE

Becoming A Living Sacrifice

By Josie Kastendieck

TRILOGY

Fit to Serve: Becoming a Living Sacrifice
Trilogy Christian Publishers A Wholly Owned Subsidiary of Trinity Broadcasting Network
2442 Michelle Drive Tustin, CA 92780

10 9 8 7 6 5 4 3 2 1
Library of Congress Cataloging-in-Publication Data is available.

ISBN: 978-1-68556-516-9
E-ISBN: 978-1-68556-517-6

DEDICATION

To the greatest gift I've ever received: my faith in Jesus Christ.

To my best friend who has cheered me on every step of the way, my husband.

To my greatest role models who have taught me the value of hard work. Thanks, Mom and Dad!

ACKNOWLEDGMENTS

To my adventure buddy, best friend, and husband, Joseph. You've been there for me in more ways than I deserved. You've loved me past my expectations, and you've been the godly encouragement I've always needed.

Thank you for your sacrifices and belief in me. To the moon and back.

Mom and Dad: Thank you for always believing in me no matter where I decide to go. Thank you for all the years you've prayed for me and guided me in my life. My biggest honor in my life is to call you Mom and Dad. I love you.

To my siblings: Molly, Travis, Amethyst, Andrew, and Kate. My favorite memories are of all of us laughing until we cry. I can't explain how special each of you is to me. I can't wait for more late-night shenanigans with you all. Love you guys.

Kastendieck family: Not only did you raise the perfect son to become my husband, but you've been the perfect in-law family that I could never have dreamed of. All of your love, support, unrelenting kindness, enthusiasm, wisdom, and godly encouragement have meant the world to me. I love you all.

Bekah: You and Erik will always be family. God knew I needed your friendship, and I can't imagine where I would be today without you. Thank you for being the godly influence in my life. I love you.

Kim: From start to finish, you've always been there. Thick and thin. I've always known I could count on you. Thank you for always being there for me and growing through this life together with me.

Eric: God truly gave you a gift to push others to success. You've been that big brother to me that's never been afraid to give it to me straight. I'm so grateful for your teaching, your impossibly loud laughter, and your friendship through the years.

Lisa: You've been that partner in crime I've always needed. Joe and I can't thank you enough for what you've done for us. We are so grateful to have your love and support. We love you!

TBN Publishing: Thank you for keeping God first in every step of publishing. I'm so grateful for your excellence and passion in publishing.

Lastly, to all the friends and family that have been supporters of my journey. Your love has meant everything to me, and I could never have come this far without you. Thank you all.

TABLE OF CONTENTS

PREFACE

Therefore, I urge you, brothers and sisters, in view of God's mercy, to offer your bodies as a living sacrifice, holy and pleasing to God-this is true and proper worship. Do not conform to the pattern of this world, but be transformed by the renewing of your mind. Then you will be able to test and approve what God's will is—his good, pleasing and perfect will.

Romans 12:1–2

Here I was, on this journey of being a newlywed, trying to find a job, having relocated to a new state, and adjusting to the military lifestyle. There were so many aspects of my life that were thrown off kilter by a mile as I had uprooted my whole normal way of living. I would do it again in a heartbeat, mind you. I loved the excitement that a new life offered me. I loved learning how to be a wife to my husband, but I felt completely overwhelmed at the prospect of trying to figure out what I was supposed to do with my life.

I was a graduate of Colorado Mesa University with a bachelor's in kinesiology that focused on health and fitness. I knew I had a deep love for all things health and fitness related as well as teaching, but God had another route than for me to become a PE teacher. So then I switched to a more broad degree, kinesiology. It gave me the ability to have several career paths that made the most sense to me as I was becoming a military wife. However, I never foresaw the trepidation I would have trying to find an area of fitness and health that wasn't so commercialized. A career in health and fitness that wasn't so focused on making oodles of money instead of actually helping people. It was like I yearned for a combination of healthy living and how to teach it while doing it in a way that was like being a missionary. I wanted God to be the center of what I taught, not just science. I wanted to share the gospel with people while teaching them to be healthy. Nowhere did I see a career field that laid the way for me.

It was one morning in my routine of submitting job applications that a thought hit me out of nowhere. I felt a tug on my heart from God to write a book combining biblical application with my passion for health and fitness. I immediately tossed the thought aside, as I was not a writer, nor had I any aspiration to be. After a few weeks of the same thought badgering my thoughts, I finally spent time in prayer to seek some wisdom. Wouldn't you know that I felt a total peace to dive into writing a book?

Time passed, as it took me a year to find out what information I wanted to include. I sorted through the basics of health and fitness to find the most simplistic yet most important health information that people really needed to hear. I also had to figure out where my heart was for wanting to teach the biblical side. I had never had any proper schooling in the Bible, but that didn't slow me down, as God provided what I needed. With great help from wise friends and family, I found the tools and the research to pair Fit to Serve together. It wasn't easy, nor a walk in the park. There were encouraging times and resistant times where I had to fight against a world that didn't want me to talk about the truth God laid on my heart.

A year and a half later, this book will be lying in your hands. A place I never dreamed it would get to, but God knew this entire time. It was no accident that you came across this book. It's not for my fame or prosperity; it's simply to teach you the ways God has intended you to use your body. I hope you take to heart what God has to say to you through this book. He changed my life through it, and I pray He changes yours also.

INTRODUCTION

What is your interest in trying to read this book? Is it because you're hoping that somewhere I will show you the newest and best weight loss trick? Maybe you want to see how to combine fitness and faith and are looking for a simple way to combine them. Perhaps you're hoping I don't have any biblical connections so that you don't have to feel bad about not exercising. Here's the truth, nowhere in the Bible does it actually talk about fitness.

For those of you who don't like exercising, you're probably feeling elated. For those of you who enjoy it, maybe not so much. Here's the catch, the Bible talks about what not to do with your body. It shows us how to honor God by taking care of your body and not letting it fall into sin (Romans 6:12–14, 15–16, 19). So here we are; this can apply to all of you! Maybe that's not what you want to hear, so why would you even want to read this book? Read this book because I will show you how toxic and sinful our fitness industry has turned today. I will show you how modern-day Christians are falling into the lustful, greedy, jealous, idolatry-like traps that have been laid for them through fitness.

For those of you that have been letting laziness take over your lives and bodies, know this—God meant for us to take care of our bodies so that we can be used to do His will, to praise Him, and glorify Him in the way He designed us to be.

Don't invite that insufferable tyrant of sin back into your mortal body so you won't become obedient to its destructive desires. Don't offer your bodily members to sin's service as tools of wickedness; instead, offer your body to God as those who are alive from the dead, and devote the parts of your body to God as tools for justice and goodness in this world.

Romans 6:12–13

So don't think of this book as a "faith and fitness" type of book, but instead think of it as a book that shows you how to make yourselves a living sacrifice, a temple for God.

Read Romans 12:1–2 again. Paul is writing a letter to the church in Rome instructing the body (the church) how to live for Christ. In this beautiful passage, he explains how powerful the gospel is and how important it is for believers to follow the gospel. Paul urges his readers to start using themselves as "living sacrifices" by using their bodies—eyes, ears, mouths, hands, and feet. He does not want us to become wrapped up in the world and its wicked values. Instead, he asks us to constantly be renewing our minds so that we may be molded for Christ. When God spoke through Paul to write Romans 12:1–2, I don't think he intended for us to think, *Renew your mind and present your body as a living sacrifice but don't worry about the health of*

14

your body. How ignorant of God's gifts can we be? Yes, our bodies are full of sinful flesh, but that doesn't mean that our bodies have no value. God has used people time and time again to physically find and reach others for His glory. Think of apostle Paul, Martin Luther King Jr., Billy Graham, King David, and the list is endless. God has and is using people to *"Go out and make disciples in all the nations…Then disciple them. Form them in the practices and postures that I have taught you, and show them how to follow the commands I have laid down for you"* (Matthew 28:19–20).

We are not going to make disciples or reach God's people by being couch potatoes. God has given us usable bodies for a reason, and I don't think He intended us to not take care of them. To let us depreciate the amazing physical abilities He gave us. So please, read this book so that we can learn how to protect God's temple and how to serve Him as a living sacrifice.

SECTION 1:

BIBLICAL EVIDENCE AND DIRECTION

Chapter 1

A PERFECT PLAN

A young girl, sixteen years old, walks by her bedroom mirror only to stop and stare at what she sees. She looks at her growing body and despises that it doesn't look like the Victoria's Secret model on the cover of the magazines she keeps hidden under her bed. She thinks that no boy will ever find her attractive.

A middle-aged mom struggles day in and day out to keep her family running while she barely can. In the middle of burping her baby and picking up after her toddler, she thinks to herself that she's not doing half bad, that she's a good mom and wife. But then she looks down and sees the extra weight around her middle, her hips, legs, and everywhere else. She's immediately discouraged and crushed because she now thinks of herself as ugly, fat, unlovable, and even maybe a terrible mom.

A teen boy that's made of skin and bones tries to lift heavy weights like his bigger built football buddies. The weight is too much, and he fails to lift it, which brings a roar of laughter from his teammates. There is endless teasing about how skinny and weak he is. He goes home to look at his body and loathes what he sees in the mirror. Why can't he be more muscular and strong like them?

A busy, hard-working husband and father of three drags his feet in the door to meet the ever-energetic kids that seem to never slow down. Tiredly he joins in on playtime, dinner, then bedtime. Finally, as he winds down for bed, he goes to brush his teeth. As he looks in the mirror, he looks at his out-of-shape body. He feels ashamed and embarrassed that he's not the man he was in his twenties.

A young married couple who are now starting to wind out of their honeymoon phase suddenly starts to see physical areas that they wouldn't let show before. *Will he still like me the way he did when we got married even though I've started to put on weight? Will she still adore me even though I've lost some muscle?* Do or did any of these stories sound familiar to you?

What about the college-aged young men and women so pressured by their peers around them to fit in and find love? They struggle because they will allow lies about their appearance to take over. That she's not pretty enough, skinny enough. That he isn't handsome enough, cool enough, or fit. They believe these lies so much that one of them will think about taking their own life because that would be easier than dealing with the pain of not being perfect.

These aren't just stories; these are real situations of people I know. These people are just like you and me; we find faults in our own health and take it so far to think we'll never be perfect. I wrote this book for you, for all of you that think the way that evil wants you to think, so you will never see the true beauty of God's creation.

So You're Not Perfect?

Maybe you've had times of struggle like the stories above. Maybe today you've let yourself slide down that slippery slope of disgust towards yourself. We've all been there more than once. It's a way Satan lies to us, making us feel as though we'll never be enough, that we'll never be perfect. He is that liar in our head that makes us believe horrible things about ourselves. He makes us believe so many things that we forget that we never had to be perfect because we have a perfect Savior. Our version of perfect is this world's version that makes us strive after our flesh and encourages lustful perfection that God never designed us to be or wants us to long after. This world tries to convince us that being thin or muscular is what makes us beautiful, but God thinks of us as beautiful no matter how we look. One thing is true; you'll never be perfect. Why? Because we have a loving and merciful heavenly Father that is completely perfect. If we were perfect, we wouldn't need God! He designed us to be less than perfect so we would need to rely on Him and submit to Him. His design, you, are perfectly made the way He planned you to be. You are no surprise to God because He formed you before you were even born. *"Before I formed you in the womb I knew you, and before you were born I consecrated you; I appointed you a prophet to the nations"* (Jeremiah 1:5). How could a powerful, loving God make a mistake with you? He didn't "forget" some things like maybe a six-pack or a pear-shaped body, bigger chest, or less weight around your middle. The world has poisoned us now to think we need these things, but God tells us differently.

As for you, don't you remember how you used to just exist? Corpses, dead in life, buried by transgressions, wandering the course of this perverse world. You were the offspring of the prince of the power of air—oh, how he owned you, just as he still controls those living in disobedience. I'm not talking about the outsiders alone; we were all guilty of falling headlong for the persuasive passions of this world; we all have had our fill of indulging the flesh and mind, obeying impulses to follow perverse thoughts motivated by dark powers. As a result, our natural inclinations led us to be children of wrath, just like the rest of humankind. But God, with the unfathomable richness of His love and mercy focused on us, united us with the Anointed One and infused our lifeless souls with life—even though we were buried under mountains of sin—and saved us by His grace. He raised us up with Him and seated us in the heavenly realms with our beloved Jesus the Anointed, the Liberating King. He did this for a reason: so that for all eternity we will stand as a living testimony to the incredible riches of His grace and kindness that He freely gives to us by uniting us with Jesus the Anointed. For it's by God's grace that you have been saved. You receive it through faith. It was not our plan or our effort. It is God's gift, pure and simple. You didn't earn it, not one of us did, so don't go around bragging that you must have done something amazing. For we are the product of His hand, heaven's poetry etched on lives, created in the Anointed, Jesus, to accomplish the good works God arranged long ago.

Ephesians 2:1–10

In this passage, Paul is speaking to the Ephesians while he is imprisoned. As he is in captivity, he shares this encouraging message that tells us that we are God's craftsmanship, created to do His good works. Before we were even born, God knew exactly what He made each and everyone one of us for. Nothing God created was wrong or imperfect. Everything, including us, was good. *"And God saw everything he had made, and behold, it was very good"* (Genesis 1:31). We see through His Word that He has made us perfectly, just the way He planned for us to be. In Ephesians 2, however, we see how our sinful flesh, how Satan, is constantly at work to make us stumble. He is ever-so consistent to make us think less of ourselves so that we never feel worthy of God's love, of Jesus' sacrifice. Later in the passage, however, Paul explains that by grace only have we been saved through faith, which is a gift from God. So what does all this mean? Am I perfect, or am I not? Well, I'm simply saying this, when looking in terms of the world and all of its sinfulness, we will never be perfect, nor should we try to be in its standards, but, in God's eyes, He has made us exactly how He wants us. We are His perfect creation, and it's time to stop letting the lies of this world tell us to think differently. It's time to accept the fact that we will never be perfect for the world, and we shouldn't have to be. It's time to start believing God's Word that we are His perfect creation and should live this life trying to live for Him instead.

Slippery Slope of Doubt

Many people have the strategy that if they always anticipate the worst outcome in any situation, then they will never be disappointed if it doesn't happen. We tend to think the same way when our bodies are concerned. A new diet, a different workout routine, a magic drink mixture, unheard-of fruit that magically burns belly fat from a doctor no one's heard about, instant weight loss pills, a vibrating contracting machine to give you abs, the list goes on. All of these things you give a try, waiting to see if you've truly found the secret in the weight loss community, but deep down, you don't expect it to change, and you still despise the way you look.

This thinking, this ugly cycle we put ourselves through, is so destructive, and it is a gateway for the liar to enter our thinking as we tear down God's creation. When one unhealthy thought surfaces and you tell yourself it's true, you're letting the devil tell you that you're not good enough and that you should just give up. This negative way of thinking is so addicting because it's easier to give in to doubt instead of fighting it.

Why do so many people start a workout program with great ferocity, and then two months later, they are already throwing in the towel? Why does the mom of three kids experiment with a new diet, feeling optimistic about change, then hit rock bottom when life gets hard and drops the program? Eric Worre talks about choosing your hard, *"Marriage is hard, divorce is hard, choose your hard. Being an entrepreneur is hard, being an employee* is hard, choose your hard. Being obese is hard, staying in shape is hard, choose your hard."

When you start down that slope of doubt, it is so hard to climb back up. Not only do we have to overcome those negative thoughts and feelings, but we have to let go of the addiction of feeling sorry for ourselves. It's easy to take pity on yourself, telling yourself excuse after excuse why you can't do it, but truly the hardest task of all to finally take responsibility for where you are at is making that change. God tells us, "...*whatever is true, whatever is noble, whatever is right, whatever is pure, whatever is lovely, whatever is admirable—if anything is excellent or praiseworthy—think about such things*" (Philippians 4:8). This is how God asks us to think! So why would you dishonor God by allowing yourself hateful thoughts about His own creation?

Count it all joy, my brothers, when you meet trials of various kinds, for you know that the testing of your faith produces steadfastness. And let steadfastness have its full effect, that you may be perfect and complete, lacking in nothing. If any of you lacks wisdom, let him ask God, who give generously to all without reproach, and it will be given him. But let him ask in faith, with no doubting, for the one who doubts is like a wave of the sea that is driven and tossed by the wind. For that person must not suppose that he will receive anything from the Lord; he is a double-minded man, unstable in all his ways. Let the lowly brother boast in his exaltation, and the rich in his humiliation, because like a flower of the grass he will pass away. For the sun rises with its scorching heat and withers the grass; its flower falls, and its beauty perishes. So also will the rich man fade away in the modest of his pursuits. Blessed is the man who remains steadfast under trail, for when he has stood the test he will receive the crown of life, which God has promised to those who love him. Let no one say when he is tempted,

"I am being tempted by God," for God cannot be tempted with evil, and he himself tempts no one. But each person is tempted when he is lured and enticed by his own desire. Then desire when it has conceived gives birth to sin, and sin when it is fully grows brings forth death. Do not be deceived, my believed brothers. Every good gift and every perfect gift is from above, coming down from the Father of lights, with whom there is no variation or shadow due to change. Of his own will he brought us forth by the worth of truth, that we should be a kind of firstfruits of his creatures.

James 1:2–18

This may be a long passage to read, but reread if you need to, to really absorb what James is telling you. This is a powerful passage that hits us deep where all of us struggle daily. When James addresses believers about their daily walk with God and trusting in Him through all trials, he specifically emphasizes on *"count it all joy"* when life happens. Life, the daily struggles we all go through as we are constantly tempted by the prince of the earth to sin against God. James means that whatever the daily struggle is that you go through, whether it be mental, physical, or spiritual, we count all of those struggles as joy. Even the struggles we go through with our bodies daily are one to count as joy. The Bible is God-breathed. There are no mistakes, and that means God meant this passage perfectly how it is and that He meant your body is perfect as it is. So what does this all mean? It means it's time to finally stand up and stop letting yourself get sucked into the addicting and hateful world of doubt. It's time to start believing that you were made perfectly from head to toe and start using your body as a tool for Christ.

Be Grateful for What You Have

"And God said, Let us make man in our image, after our likeness..." (Genesis 1:26). Take a minute to look at yourself in the mirror. Have you ever stopped to think that you are a recreation of our heavenly Father? That you were designed based after God Himself? God has made every single one of us based on His image. He is perfect in every way; He makes no mistakes, and that includes the way your body was designed.

This generation is so focused on changing ourselves based on what we think we should look like, and we take it so far that we make ourselves into a whole different person. We do this by surgery, medication, makeup, clothing, medical treatments, and the list is ongoing. I can't imagine how sad this change makes God when we decide we are going to modify how we look, how He made us.

One time, I was staying at a very tall hotel for a vacation. I was bringing some groceries to our room and decided to hop in the elevator. Once inside, a mother and her child joined me. I noticed that the child had Down's syndrome. But let me tell you, that child was one of the most beautiful little girls I had ever laid eyes on. She had on a striped bathing suit, two puffy arm floaties, goggles, and her hair was split into two pigtails. I couldn't keep from smiling as her presence was so contagious. I waved, and the little girl waved back. There was

25

no secret that this little girl and her mother were wrapped around each other's fingers. That mom loved that little girl with all of her heart, even with Down's syndrome. I imagine the mother didn't even care that she had Down's because to her, she was perfect; she was her child.

I imagine this is how our heavenly Father feels about us and how we look. We are absolutely beautiful to Him, inside and out. But imagine if that child from my story grew up and decided to alter herself to look more "normal." Her mother would be devastated to see her little girl change her beautiful self. I think God feels the same way when we decide we will change ourselves to finally give us that missing piece we've always longed for; I know it breaks His heart. The only piece you will find if you travel down this dangerous road is filled with temptation, sin, and hate. This road is all-consuming because whatever you do will never be enough; you will always want something more. The only way you will fill that hole in your heart is by trusting God that you look exactly the way you were meant to. *"I praise you, for I am fearfully and wonderfully made. Wonderful are your works; my soul knows it very well"* (Psalm 139:14).

It's time we stop letting ourselves believe the lies of this sinful world that physical change will make us feel more beautiful. Instead, it's time to start being grateful for what we have, to be thankful that God has made us fearfully and wonderfully.

In college, I had the pleasure of assisting a personal trainer that organized a group of disabled individuals. Some couldn't physically talk; others had Down's syndrome, and most of them had a physical disability that didn't allow them to move their body efficiently. One of my favorite individuals I had the pleasure of working with was a young woman in high school; let's call her Libby. She had been born with a disorder that limited her limbs to never fully grow. Her two arms were much shorter than average, and they did not fully grow into adult length. She could still move her arms to do tasks normally like you and I, but she did have to modify several activities for herself. Even though she may have had a disability, Libby never let herself see it as one. Instead, she saw it as a challenge to be conquered, and she pushed herself physically every day to grow stronger. She was the light of every room you walked into with the biggest smile on her face. You would never think for a second that she was any less than you or me.

Libby went on to swim for the Special Olympics, where she placed numerous times. She pushed herself harder and harder every session because she wanted to get better and be stronger. It never seemed to phase her that she had a disability. Instead, she always put on her winning smile and did her best. We need a mindset like Libby's. We need to use what we do have and be grateful for it instead of whining about what we don't have or can't do. I guarantee there's someone out there that physically can't do what you can but is working harder than you and is thankful for what they do have. So maybe it's time to stop feeling sorry for yourself and start being grateful.

Every time I finish working out, I like to end my session by stretching and praying silently to myself. Even if I feel like I didn't have a great workout or I am not growing in the ways I want, I take that time to thank God for this body He has given me. I start thinking about what I do have instead of what I don't. I start off by thinking of what things I may take for granted. I have a working body that can move my arms and legs without struggle or pain. I have strength in my body to perform movements that make me healthier when I know that others do not. I have the energy to be present and work hard in life, which I know is God-given. Lastly, I like to thank my heavenly Father that He has given me a body to train and improve so that I can be ready to use it for His glory, whatever that may be.

Next time you're struggling about the look of your body, or you start to degrade what you have, take a few minutes to stop and think about what you have instead of what you don't. Take that time to thank God for all of the things He has given you physically. He's graced you with this body; it's time to start taking care of it. It's time to be grateful for what you have.

Chapter 2

A CONTENT HEART

Someone in the crowd said to him [Jesus], "Teacher, tell my brother to divide the inheritance with me." But he said to him, "Man, who made me a judge or arbitrator over you?" And he said to them, "Take care, and be on your guard against all covetousness, for one's life does not consist in the abundance of his possessions." And he told them a parable, saying, "The land of a rich man produced plentifully, and he thought to himself, 'What shall I do, for I have nowhere to store my crops?' And he said, 'I will do this: I will tear down my barns and build larger ones, and there I will store all my grain and goods. And I will say to my soul, "Soul, you have ample goods laid up for many years; relax, eat, drink be merry." But God said to him, 'Fool! This night your soul is required of you, and the things you have prepared, whose will they be?' So is the one who lays up treasure for himself and is not rich toward God."

Luke 12:13–21

This section of Luke is talking about the parable of the rich man who is a fool. The fool demonstrates a man that tries to build his wealth on earth, but after God rebukes him, he is told that he can't take any of his earthly belongings to heaven. He only can take his soul, which he has not bothered to build up for the Lord. The part I really want you to pay special attention to is, "...*be on guard against all covetousness...*" "Covetousness" means "to have eager or excessive desire, usually pertaining to wealth or possessions."

> *But godliness with contentment is great gain. For we brought nothing into the world, and we can take nothing out of it. But if we have food and clothing, we will be content with that. Those who want to get rich fall into temptation and a trap and into many foolish and harmful desires that plunge people into ruin and destruction.*

> 1 Timothy 6:6–9

First Timothy 6:6–9 now talks about in detail how we cannot bring anything from this earth to heaven. Those who yearn after riches will ultimately destroy themselves as they fall into a world of sin. But those who strive after contentment are honoring God.

So what is the commonality of the two passages? Honestly, there are many good things to take away, but the one I want to draw your attention to is contentment. "Contentment" means "to be satisfied or pleased." Back when these were written, people had less riches than we do now, yet they were still told to be content with what they had. How much more do this day and age have in relation to riches? The temptation to be unsatisfied is normalized now, and it's actually on the rise and out of control. Social media constantly makes us compare ourselves to someone or something else so that we feel so insecure about what we have that we feel obligated to buy whatever product they're trying to sell. Marketplaces now have perfected preying on people's insecurities to make them feel even worse about themselves just to make a couple of bucks. We are all guilty of playing this uncontent game; I know I am.

Back in my college days during my freshman year, I struggled (as did many during this time) with gaining some extra weight that I didn't need. Back then, it was coined the "freshman fifteen," as that was the amount of extra weight that most young people would gain from being introduced into college life. I didn't put on fifteen but only five or ten. I remember feeling so embarrassed. I was athletic, played sports, thrived in a fitness community, and was pursuing a degree in the health industry, yet I had allowed myself to go down that road. I allowed myself to gain extra weight I didn't need. I remember feeling so unsatisfied with how I looked that I let myself fall into "senseless and harmful desires" of wanting to have that perfect body. I desired after the girls I saw on social media that looked perfect, and oh how I wished I looked like them. One day after scrolling for who knows how long on Facebook, I remember seeing an advertisement for this magic weight loss pill that instantly made you lose weight and feel amazing. Hundreds of people tried this product and had amazing results. Wow! I was so drawn in by this advertisement that within ten minutes, I had ordered that silly bottle of pills and anxiously awaited its delivery. For a pack of thirty pills, this bottle cost $59.99. Not exactly a cheap option for a simple college student, but in my mind, it was worth every penny. After thirty days, you can imagine that I didn't see one single result with those silly sugar pills. Every morning I'd race to the scale to see if it had done any of its magic just to be disappointed that I was still in the same shape I was before. One day, I had contemplated buying a second bottle in hopes that I just needed more time to see my results. That was until God put a conviction in my heart that I needed to find my answer in contentment, not in a bottle full of faux pills. So instead, I started seeking the Lord more earnestly in prayer and study time, and instead of feeling sorry for myself with the weight, I suddenly had the motivation to start attending the gym and become aware of my health habits. Over time, I lost the extra weight I had gained, but I didn't even notice because instead, I was focused on God, who taught me to be content with how I looked. God finally changed my perspective. He showed me how to love myself for who He made me to be instead of believing the lies of this world.

I still struggle with letting go of my insecurities, not comparing myself to others, and avoiding the temptations of social media. But I know God had a plan for allowing me to go through that phase in my life. I needed to learn how to put things in perspective and put God first. I needed to learn how to be content. Maybe contentment is something you struggle with too. It's okay to be struggling, but it's time to stop finding excuses and to start pursuing God.

The Comparison Game

The first step for honoring God with your bodies for the temple He has made is to be grateful for what He gave you. Every single flaw that you see is perfect in God's eyes. Our society today has convinced us what perfect looks like, and anything less than that, we are now trained to want to fix it. Especially in the fitness industry! I'm a big proponent for health and fitness, but I disdain the way fitness is advertised to people. Constantly, advertisements will show very fit men or women using a device or magic supplement that instantly makes them look the way they do. They make these advertisements so that you see how the models look, desire to look like them, and are fooled into buying yet another pointless money maker that you will eventually forget in your closet.

Here's an example: a year or two ago, someone came out with this "instant ab maker." It's a device that sticks to your torso, contracts your muscles, and makes abs without you even having to work for them. Ridiculous! I knew plenty of friends that were tempted to buy it and probably did end up wasting their money on it. Those friends felt insecure about their weight and abdominals, sought the easiest solution, and prayed for the effect of an amazing loophole to get results without them spending hard hours of work to get them. Well, let me tell you something, if you were to look up that product and find the actual articles or journals associated with it stating they have tested and proved it, you would find very little. Those friends of mine that may have bought it were probably very disappointed to see their product gave no results. It's a money-making scam, just like hundreds of other products out there. Thank goodness we have something we know we can always rely on: God's Word.

"You therefore must be perfect, as your heavenly Father is perfect"

33

(Matthew 5:48).

"I praise you, for I am fearfully and wonderfully made. Wonderful are your works; my soul knows it very well" (Psalm 139:14).

"For we are his workmanship, created in Christ Jesus for good works, which God prepared beforehand, that we should walk in them" (Ephesians 2:10).

"So God created man in his own image, in the image of God he created him; male and female he created them" (Genesis 1:27).

"But he said to me, 'My grace is sufficient for you, for my power is made perfect in weakness.' Therefore I will boast all the more gladly of my weakness, so that the power of Christ may rest upon me" (2 Corinthians 12:9).

God's Word is full of passages that talk about how His designs are absolutely perfect. So why do we let this world convince us that we are less than what God tells us? It's because we are trained by outside sources to think that those who look "perfect" must be happier than we are. Let me tell you about people who are on the front page of fitness magazines or stars on social media. These models, body-builders, and fitness gurus don't get to live a normal life. Their whole world revolves around fitness. Their life revolves around how much activity they put in their day, how much time at the gym, exactly what foods they eat and how much, constantly checking their body fat percentage, looking at themselves in the mirror, and making sure certain clothing articles fit perfectly. There's nothing happy or healthy about their routine. Many models struggle with anorexia, bulimia, muscle dysmorphia, psychological disorders, anxiety, stress, and even depression. All because they are obsessed with achieving the perfect look. Here's a secret, many of them are unhappy because they always feel like there's another level to achieve, so they must train harder, diet more rigidly. It is an unhealthy, unhappy cycle that continues on and on, no matter what they do. It will never be enough. It's time to start realizing what you have right in front of you, not what some magazine or social media claim you should have.

I want to encourage you to take a little time to write down all the things you're insecure about or feel like you compare constantly. Then spend some time in prayer to surrender all those insecurities to God and let Him take care of you.

Finding Contentment in Your Making

It's true; I'm writing this book to encourage you to serve God by taking care of your body. So why would I try to tell you to be content about yourself if you're not taking care of your body? The answer is simply this; I believe that if your heart's not in the right mindset about taking care of your body, then you will never take care of your body in the right way for the service of the Lord. Remember what the Bible says about earthly possessions? *"What good will it be for someone to gain the whole world, yet forfeit their soul? Or what can anyone give in exchange for their soul?"* (Matthew 16:26) One day, we will all stand before God, and we won't have one thing from earth with us. He won't care if we have biceps, triceps, or a six-pack. Those are earthly aspirations, not heavenly ones. God seeks after our soul, not our bodies. So yes, we need to be in the right mindset because if we don't, we will end up seeking an earthly possession that doesn't honor God, and we can't even keep it.

Let's face facts here; we are all tempted to want that perfect body so that we can get those stares, the oos and aahhs from other people. We want some random stranger, family, and friends to mention how good we look. We desire to be appreciated and sought after because we think this is how we'll feel good about ourselves. These lustful, evil thoughts are exactly why we as Christians need to get our mindsets in the right place first to prevent going down a road we don't need to walk.

Here's my instruction: walk in the Spirit, and let the Spirit bring order to your life. If you do, you will never give in to your selfish and sinful cravings. For everything the flesh desires goes against the Spirit, and everything the Spirit desires goes against the flesh. There is a constant battle raging between them that prevents you from doing the good you want to do. But when you are led by the Spirit, you are no longer subject to the law. It's clear that our flesh entices us into practicing some of its most heinous acts: participating in corrupt sexual relationships, impurity, unbridled lust, idolatry, witchcraft, hatred, arguing, jealousy, anger, selfishness, contentiousness, division, envy of others good fortune, drunkenness, drunken revelry, and other shameful vices that plague humankind. I told you this clearly before, and I only tell you again so there is no room for confusion: those who give in to these ways will not inherit the kingdom of God.

Galatians 5:16–21

In this passage in Galatians, Paul is clarifying to a group of Christians that even though they may be saved through Christ Jesus, their sin is not justified by faith in Christ. People, including us today, think Christ's sacrifice has won us freedom to do what we desire. However, Paul makes it abundantly clear that Christ's sacrifice was to give us freedom to serve each other in love. So let me ask you this, do your fitness aspirations point towards loving people or loving yourself? Let's look at how the fitness industry and our sinful flesh lead us towards some of the heinous acts Paul speaks about.

» Impurity: Do your looks or the looks you wish you had make you dream of leading someone into an impure act with you physically?

» Unbridled lust: Have you experienced an uncontrollable lust towards those who are attractive physically or want to be someone that makes people feel that way about you?

» What about idolatry? I bet you didn't think this one would be an issue, but people, wake up! We are literally worshiping fit people via Instagram, Facebook, and pretty much any fitness line you see. We even get so into our heads that we start worshiping our own bodies if we think we look the right part!

37

» Hatred, anger, and jealousy: All three of these acts work together. Think back, have you ever disliked someone for how good they look? Maybe you've given them the stink eye because they're too pretty, way too handsome, or annoyingly fit. I know I have more than once.

» Arguing and contentiousness: If there was a penny for every argument started by someone's insecurity and defense mechanism, we would all probably be quite wealthy. Health and fitness is not always an easy subject to talk about with people, and it tends to be quite controversial.

» Division: Think back to high school. How many kids grouped in cliques because they were the jocks, the athletic kids compared to those who weren't? We still do it in our adult lives as well, and it divides us from fellow Christians.

» Envy of others' good fortune: This one almost doesn't need explaining. Tying right into hatred, anger, and jealousy, the envy of others' good fortune can be despising someone for the good genes they have. The fast metabolism they were born with. God made them that way, but when do we actually stop and think that instead of our usual envious response? Are you starting to notice a pattern here? How many of these are all in a vicious cycle?

Now that we can see how evil our hearts can be in the health and fitness world, it's time to get your heart right. It's time for you to find contentment for who God made you to be. True contentment comes from a heart that is dedicated to serving the Lord, and only then can we serve others.

"The Holy Spirit produces a different kind of fruit: unconditional love, joy, peace, patience, kindheartedness, goodness, faithfulness, gentleness, and self-control..." (Galatians 5:22)

Chapter 3

BEING A GOOD STEWARD

"And he who had received the five talents came forward, bringing five talents more, saying, 'Master, you delivered to me five talents; here, I have made five talents more.' His master said to him, 'Well done, good and faithful servant. You have been faithful over a little; I will set you over much. Enter into the joy of your master."

Matthew 25:20–21

I encourage you to read the whole story about the master and his three servants in Matthew 25:14–30. It is a very powerful illustration of Jesus, who is the Master, and His servants, who are us. The point of this parable is to communicate how Jesus's servants should live while they are awaiting His return. The story talks about a certain amount of talents (money). When the master returns from his journey, he begins to settle accounts with the servants to see what they did with the talents he left them.

A really wise friend of mine once preached a sermon on this message. He used the example that in today's world, Jesus has given us each a talent or several talents. A talent is something we can use for His honor and glory. My friend deeply challenged the church by asking them, "What are you going to use your talents for? Will you hide them like the wicked and slothful servant? Or will you be like the good and faithful servant that takes a little and earns much more for his master?" This passage is so convicting because not only does it remind us how we are to live and use the talents God has given each of us, but it also challenges us to be good stewards of what we have been given. In the previous chapters, we've learned that our bodies are God-given; they are perfect. So why would we not be good stewards of our bodies? Why would we not use the talents God's given us to serve Him even more? I would like to share with you the different talents that I think God has given us to glorify Him with our bodies.

Talent 1—Is Your Mind Set on Fleshly Desires?

> *For what the law was powerless to do because it was weakened by the flesh, God did by sending his own Son in the likeness of sinful flesh to be a sin offering. And so he condemned sin in the flesh, in order that the righteous requirement of the law might be fully met in us, who do not live according to the flesh but according to the Spirit. Those who live according to the flesh have their minds set on what the flesh desires; but those who live in accordance with the Spirit have their minds set on what the Spirit desires. The mind governed by the flesh is hostile to God; it does not submit to God's law, nor can it do so. Those who are in the realm of the flesh cannot please God.*

> Romans 8:3–8

Whenever I'm working with a client for health coaching or personal training, I always want to know why they truly want to get in better shape. Is it because their doctor told them to, do they want to play more with their kids/grandkids, feel healthier, or is there an appetite to be desirable?

I had one friend approach me, asking if I would train her to lose some weight. I was excited at the opportunity and said yes. We started out by performing a basic consultation. I asked her why she wanted to lose weight, and her answer was that she wanted to lose weight for her husband. At the time, I felt like that was reason enough, and we started our program. Well, the program lasted only two months before she didn't want to continue. Maybe a year later, she approached me again about pursuing training, but this time, it was so she could meet the qualifications to enlist in the military. I was much more excited about this desire to train, so I agreed. We trained for three months this time, but alas, due to family circumstances, we had to stop again, and she never started back up.

I don't know whether or not she truly had other underlying reasons to train, but after the second time, I realized that we need more substantial reasons to become healthy and fit if it's really going to stick. She had the desire to train, but it wasn't a strong enough reason to continue, or maybe not a good enough one. If not for our own good to adhere more strongly to a program, our hearts also need to be in the right place so that the training will be honoring to God no matter what.

We soon gain an obsession to be just as the world would want us to be, and we justify it by posting it on social media to receive the compliments we've been dying to hear. We start following like-minded individuals to compare our progress. The way we think, the way we act, follows those we praise physically so that we can rationalize that what we're doing is fine. The world says it's fine, but God tells us differently. *"Do not be conformed to this world, but be transformed by the renewal of your mind, that by testing you may discern what is the will of God, what is good and acceptable and perfect"* (Romans 12:2).

Now we're getting to the heart of the matter. In your heart, concerning health and fitness, what is "good and acceptable and perfect"? What is your main goal? Will it honor God, or will it conform to this world?

Let me be very vulnerable with you about myself. In my middle school years, I was a complete tomboy. Basketball shorts, T-shirts, long braided hair, and I wanted nothing to do with any girly things. To make matters worse, I had my hair cut very short to be cute, but it ended up looking like Amanda Bynes's boy character from She's the Man. It wasn't pretty, believe me. Long story short, when I became a freshman in high school, I changed a lot. Longer hair, makeup, and I wore more feminine clothes. I was also participating in several sports for the first time. Not only did I pursue volleyball but track and field, along with weightlifting. A big moment for me in my puberty years was finding out I was good at being strong, fit, and athletic. I was able to lift more weights than most boys, and I was competitive at volleyball and track. Halfway through my freshman year, I remember going to sleep and placing my hands on my stomach. My eyes shot open as I realized that my stomach was really flat and lean. I never noticed it before, but there it was! I was in good shape, and I thought maybe I was attractive. As much as it pains me to view myself in my teenage brain, this is really where my mind was. Shortly after this realization, I was asked out by a couple of boys at school. I was giddy with excitement because, for the first time in my life (at least in the teenage mind), I attracted attention.

As a crazy, hormonal teenager, all the attention just made me crave more. Bless my wonderful husband's heart that he waited through all the other boy dramas and continued to be the perfect knight in shining armor. However, even though I was about to be dating this wonderful beyond measure man of my dreams, I wanted more. I wanted to look more attractive and mature. I'm sorry, Mom and Dad, but I think if all of us are honest, this is how we all feel when we're teenagers. I had the desire to be desirable! I had the most lustful heart that wanted nothing more than what the world wanted.

This memory makes me shudder with disgust looking back to my lustful self. Maybe you thought that there's no harm in that; every teenager goes through that time. They do because we normalize it! We normalize those desires at all stages of life, young or old. That's what this world tries to revolve around! Wake up, my friend! Enough with the side-stepping, excuse-making, self-justifying lies that you have rationalized in your life.

Brother or sister in Christ, please be honest with yourself in this time. I want to encourage Christ-followers to improve their health so that they can serve our heavenly Father. I want so badly for you to be able to reach that potential, to use that talent that He has laid out for you. Don't let your mind be on things of this world; let those desires go. *"Take no part in the unfruitful works of darkness, but instead expose them"* (Ephesians 5:11). Now is the time to expose your thoughts of what you have wanted for your body and instead turn your body to be a follower of God.

So how do you keep your mind on godly things while pursuing a healthier lifestyle? I tell several people I meet that the first step to thinking godly fitness thoughts is to be thankful. Thankful for the body God gave you. *"Give thanks in all circumstances; for this is God's will for you in Christ Jesus"* (1 Thessalonians 5:18).

When I'm wrapping up my workout for the day, I like to take five minutes of stretching or easy walking while plugging in my favorite worship music. During those five minutes, I spend my time thinking of all the ways my body performs: I can walk, run, lift weights, challenge myself, and grow. All actions at the gym, I try to stop and thank God for each and every one of them. He gave me arms to use, legs to walk, muscles to lift weights, and He gifted me with the energy and health to train myself today. I end my workout in prayer to thank God for the blessings He's given me.

Any of those things I mentioned previously could be taken away in the blink of an eye by a car crash, sudden health diagnosis, or misuse. He has given me the strength I needed for that day to pursue a healthy lifestyle, so while I have this body, I will give all the honor and glory to my Father in heaven. I hope you do the same.

Talent 2—Your Body Is a Temple

We've talked quite a bit about how our bodies are special to God. That even though we are only here for a short time, it's important we take care of them for the time we are allowed. So your body, a body that was *"bought at a price"* from Christ's sacrifice on the cross, is meant to serve God.

Paul rebuked the Corinthians about the sinful actions of sexual immorality because they are all sinning against Christ. Maybe you wonder why I mention a passage that deals with the sin of immorality? I bring it to your attention for simply this, *"Or do you not know that your body is a temple of the Holy Spirit within you, whom you have from God? You are not your own"* (1 Corinthians 6:19). Take a minute to think about the weight of that news that the Holy Spirit lives inside you! Even with our sinful, wretched fleshly bodies, God still loves us enough to live inside us. This is what Paul is trying to hammer home. We dishonor God by engaging in sinful activities because He lives in us. Maybe we are, or maybe we aren't pursuing sins of immorality, but we need to take care of our temples nonetheless.

I remember the first time this passage really hit home for me. I was reading during my quiet time when I had the thought of previous sins I had done. I felt sick to think that God's Holy Spirit was inside me, watching me while I sinned against Him. Immediately I became so grateful for knowing He is a forgiving and merciful Father. Thinking forward, I realized I didn't want my body to be sinful; I wanted it to serve Him. I don't want the God of the universe to live inside a sloth-ful, unhealthy, and selfish body. I want to honor Him with my temple so He can use me for whatever is in His will.

I have a friend that reached out to me to help her live a healthier life so she could safely pursue pregnancy. I still remember our first meeting, a meeting that broke my heart for this girl. She had struggled so long with eating disorders, abuse, and hate for her own body. She couldn't see a way out of her self-destructing situation. Slowly, we started implementing small habits to change the harsh routine that she had used for so long on her body. Little by little, she started seeing progress. She was eating more, feeling better, and was discovering what taking care of her body meant. I'm so glad to report now that she is pregnant. I pray that she continues to learn how to take care of the temple God has given her.

My friends, let yourself be a living sacrifice to our Father by not letting your body go to waste. You are meant to do amazing things for God, but don't let it be your lifestyle that cripples you. Instead, take care of your body, your temple, so that you can do those amazing things for God.

Talent 3—Good and Faithful Stewardship

"Let a man so account of us, as of the ministers of Christ, and stewards of the mysteries of God. Moreover it is required in stewards, that man be found faithful" (1 Corinthians 4:1–2).

This section in Luke challenges us, Jesus's followers, to be good stewards, who are servants that are mindful of Jesus's return someday. This servant will be held accountable for how they took care of what they were given and how they used it for His glory.

We now live in a world where obesity is an epidemic. We are facing around 108 million people that are obese. A hundred and eight million of those will have hypertension, and 78 million will need to take cholesterol-lowering medication. Twenty-eight million now have diabetes, and many more will be pre-diabetics. Let's also factor in the effects of the coronavirus in 2019. Those numbers have grown even more from people staying home and being inactive. In the short time we are allowed to live on earth, we are abusing and misusing our bodies. There are many other health issues besides the growing rate of people overweight and obese, but this is an issue many people want to skirt around because it can be sensitive. I realize that we all have a sensitivity about the extra five, ten, or more pounds around our middle. We can be defensive about those extra numbers on the scale. It's a hard truth, but the fact of the matter is that we are not taking care of ourselves at all. We are letting stress, depression, busy lives, inconvenience, and many other excuses justify the damage we are doing to our bodies. Oh sure, some people say, "It's only fifteen pounds; I'll start working out when my schedule gets easier." Others may say, "I like food too much to care." Believe me, I like food too, but you've only been given *one body, one life.*

"The second is this [commandment]: 'You shall love your neighbor as yourself.' There is no other commandment greater than these" (Mark 12:31).

We, as believers in Christ, have been called to love one another. We strive now to love someone no matter what size they may be, and in my heart, I also know it applies to helping those live a healthier life

49

so they can be tools of God. We can love people by also challenging them to live a better life. In today's world, people find reasons or ways to advocate for obesity, like the Body Positivity movement. Mind you, this movement isn't a bad thing to love people no matter their size, but we are excusing the fact that there are serious health risks. We are failing our brothers and sisters by not addressing our concern for their well-being.

"Iron sharpeneth iron; so a man sharpeneth the countenance of his friend" (Proverbs 27:17). *"Faithful are the wounds of a friend, but deceitful are the kisses of an enemy"* (Proverbs 27:6). These verses are ones about the principles of a relationship and what it means to truly grow our relationships by helping someone else improve their effectiveness to serve Christ. So are we really loving those around us by letting the quality of life decline because it's a delicate subject, or do we start loving by sharpening some iron?

Remember the verses from Luke about being a good servant? We have been challenged in this life to take care of each other, to be a "faithful and wise manager." God has given us this talent to care for others, to love as He loves. It's time to love those who struggle with being good stewards of their own bodies and to help them see how valuable they are to God.

It's also time to start realizing we need to be good stewards of ourselves if others are to believe what we are saying is true. In Matthew 5, known as Jesus's Sermon on the Mount, He had a massive crowd gather to hear His compelling teaching and see His miracles. In this crowd were His disciples, and He states that their lives are very valuable. The disciples are the ones that are the light in the world, and because of that, it is so very important they do the good works that God gave them.

You are the light of the world. A town built on a hill cannot be hidden. Neither do people light a lamp and put it under a bowl. Instead they put it on its stand, and it gives light to everyone in the house. In the same way, let your light shine before others, that they may see your good deeds and glorify your Father in heaven.

Matthew 5:14–16

Jesus charges His disciples, He charges us, to be the light for others to see in this world so full of darkness.

How can we affect others' lives for a healthier living if we are letting our own bodies go to waste? You may have a strong testimony, but if you cannot show how to live righteously and healthily for God, people will never believe what you have to say. So this means you, too, must also be a good steward.

My friend, is God speaking to you about the state of your steward-ship? Are you truly taking good care of your body, or are you letting each day go by without a second thought to it? It is never too late to start taking care of yourself, spiritually or physically. "*The Spirit and the bride: Come. And let everyone who hears these words say, 'Come.' And let those who thirst come. And who desires to drink, let them take and drink freely from the water of life*" (Revelation 22:17). Jesus speaks to us about the invitation through the bride, i.e., the church, for sinners to come to Christ to finally quench their thirst spiritually. He never puts an age limit, a sin counting meter, or anything to prevent us from drinking the water. He always has His arms open to you. So if you make this decision today to start growing yourself in the Lord, to start taking care of yourself, know that now is the best time. This is no surprise to God; He knew you'd start in His perfect timing. So now, spend time with God to talk about how He wants you to take care of your body, His temple.

Chapter 4

GOD'S VIEW OF A HEALTHY LIFESTYLE

" *But the fruit of the Spirit is love, joy, peace, forbearance, kindness, goodness, faithfulness, gentleness and self-control"* (Galatians 5:22–23).

In Galatians 5, Paul is writing a letter to the Galatians to clear up false truths that were taught to them by Judaizers who claimed a gospel of legalism. Paul, however, reminds them that the gospel is based on grace from Jesus's sacrifice. Through Him, we were justified and sanctified, and through Him, He wants us to live Christlike. If we follow Christ, we can grow and gain the nine fruits of the Spirit: love, joy, peace, patience, kindness, goodness, faithfulness, gentleness, and self-control.

Practicing Self-Control

You've most likely heard this passage in Galatians many times. As you should since it is how Jesus asks Christians to live their life on earth. Let me remind you, living for these fruits of the Spirit will not gain us entry into heaven; only belief and acceptance in Jesus's sacrifice can do that. Living by faith, according to God's Word, is how we follow Him and honor Him with the lives He has given us.

I want to point out a fruit of the Spirit that isn't commonly mentioned today (probably because it's a hard subject!). Self-control. Thoughts? Some of you might not have cared, others may have rolled their eyes, but some of you tightened up a bit. Why is that? I think some of us despise the words "self-control" because it is one of the hardest things we humans have to do. "Self-control": "the ability to control oneself, in particular one's emotions and desires or the expression of them in one's behavior, especially in difficult situations." This definition of "self-control" is the world's; let's take a look at the Bible's, "...*the power to keep your sin in check or the power to restrain you sin in thought, in word, in deed.*"

Many things in this life take so much self-control, but what I want to talk about is our self-control with laziness and food. This is not a secret; we are so bad at self-control when it comes to food and inactivity. We see it in everyday life, whether it's someone who has to have their Starbucks coffee every morning, someone that lives off of Taco Bell (I did for years), or maybe it's just the fact that you can't stop eating what's around you. Others struggle with inactivity. We've gotten so bent out of shape (quite literally) with the idea that we're either too busy to find time to be active or too depleted of energy. You are not alone; we all struggle with some area in our life.

Let me give you an example of bad self-control. Growing up, the Roth family was and is still known for our sugar addiction. It's like sugar almost runs through our veins. My father, a wonderful and amazing man, has the metabolism of a fifteen-year-old teenager. Basically, he can eat whatever, whenever, and however much he's feeling and not be a pound different the next day. The rest of the Roth crew, minus my oldest sister, were not blessed with such amazing metabolisms. Not that that stops us; the sugar addiction still tends to run our lives.

Any night my dad felt like eating ice cream after dinner, I was right there with him. I considered it my reward after a big job to let myself have some sort of sugary dessert. Any time we went out to eat at a restaurant, the thing to do was to order dessert. Sugar, if you will, became my Starbucks. I couldn't really function without it. It wasn't until I married my husband (who ironically has one of those amazing metabolisms as well) that I noticed how much dependence I put on sugar. Joe doesn't crave sugar but instead would rather find an apple or orange over a processed, sugary substance. At first, it was very irritating because here I was, a health and fitness major, and Mr. No-Sugar-Craving-Ever was consistently making better food choices than I was. Then, God's grace helped me humble myself, and I began to notice that Joe's good habits were a wonderful reminder for me to establish a little more self-control in my everyday eating habits. Thanks to my hubby, I'm not as addicted to sugar as I used to be. Don't get me wrong, I could still knock out the biggest bowl of ice cream in no time, but now I have mental strength that wasn't there before. I can now easily say no to sweets, and instead, I can choose to be satisfied with an apple or orange or even nothing at all.

I started noticing a pattern in my life with food after my sugar-epiphany. I was a very poor eater who was fueling my body with very poor foods. I remember one day I felt a huge weight on my heart to give all my bad eating habits to God. He convicted me about my poor self-control. I mentally wanted to listen, but my body still won by the end of the day. I had to finally get on my knees to ask for God's strength to help me overcome this ridiculous dependence on junk food. Thankfully, slowly, I am learning to be a better eater. It's not easy, but I know in my heart that God is working in me every day to fuel my body with the right foods, learn how to say no, and glorify Him with my obedience.

Do you struggle with a dependence on bad foods or drinks? Do you mindlessly graze on the food around you without a thought to it until after when you feel guilty about what you did? Or maybe you fall into the category that you didn't realize eating this way could turn into something sinful.

For the grace of God has appeared that offers salvation to all people. It teaches us to say, "No" to ungodliness and worldly passions, and to live self-controlled, upright and godly lives in this present age, while we wait for the blessed hope-the appearing of the glory of our great God and Savior, Jesus Christ.

Titus 2:11–13

Have you ever noticed that our world revolves around its dependence on the food industry? It's everywhere you go! Supermarkets, gas stations, street signs, airports, online advertisements, radio, and the list can go on! Yes, the food industry is a large money maker, so of course, they will push and shove every burger picture in the world in our faces so that we finally cave in and submit to the burger cravings. Think about all the "deals" they run to entice us financially. Buy one, get one free, happy hour, late-night hours, a percentage off for a special holiday, kids eat free, etc. The food industry is relentless, and the sad news is that we let it run our world without a single thought.

Did you know from the 1950s through the 1970s that fast food was not a normal thing? Not until the 1980s was it more popular for people to eat out, which is when obesity numbers started to rise. Beforehand, families were cooking almost all foods at home and were more careful about serving sizes. Now, the temptation of junk food is even worse because we can buy premade everything for home, so we don't have to make it, i.e., the true birth of the "convenience store."

Why am I bringing all of these facts up? I'm not trying to start a whole group of followers to revolt against the world's food industry or something wild like that. I'm simply showing the facts that we are now a *gluttonous people*. Did that sting a little? Don't worry; it's not just you. You may be feeling a little guilty of it, as am I, and there are hundreds of millions of other people that should wake up from their crazed food reality. But I don't call you out on it to make you feel miserable; I'm being blunt to raise your awareness so that you can do something about it! God doesn't want us to waste our short lives being gluttons; in fact, He hates it.

"Their destiny is destruction, their god is their stomach, and their glory is in their shame. Their mind is set on earthly things" (Philippians 3:19).

"Rather, clothe yourselves with the Lord Jesus Christ, and do not think about how to gratify the desires of the flesh" (Romans 13:14).

"Do not join those who drink too much wine or gorge themselves on meat, for drunkards and gluttons become poor, and drowsiness clothes them in rags" (Proverbs 23:20–21).

Heard enough? We could go round and round about the fact that our world today revolves sadly around one word, "gluttony." God knew we would struggle with gluttony; that's why in His amazing Word, He wrote how to live apart from it before fast food was even invented! Of course, gluttony doesn't just mean food, but many things like money, power, pride, possessions. Our God is truly an amazing God because He knew we would need His help to say no to gluttony but yes to the fruits of the Spirit. If you struggle with self-control, join me in prayer to ask God to turn your heart in the right direction.

"Lord, I come to You now with a heavy heart. I now realize that I'm living a selfish, gluttonous lifestyle. Forgive me for living a way that does not honor or praise You, but I want that to change today. I admit I can't do this on my own, for my strength is not my own. With You, Lord, I know that I can conquer anything. Help me to conquer my flesh today, give me the strength to learn self-control in all areas of my life, even my eating habits. I want to use this temple as your living sacrifice. Guide me today to honor You with this life. With all my heart, amen."

Staying Ready for Usefulness

We've talked about the value of self-control in our physical lives. We've also touched on subjects like good stewardship, but one I want to bring to your attention is to keep your body ready for usefulness.

"On the other hand, discipline yourself for the purpose of godliness; for bodily discipline is only of little profit, but godliness is profitable for all things, since it holds promise for the present life and also for the life to come" (1 Timothy 4:7–8). We know that Paul talks about how athletes will use self-control to win a perishable prize, but Christians are disciplining themselves spiritually for a prize that never perishes (1 Corinthians 9:25). So what am I trying to point out? Taking care of your body is important, but it should never be our first priority like we talked about in "Chapter 2: A Content Heart." But that small portion of physical fitness is what we need to take care of so that we are always ready to be useful for God.

It's true, your current role in life may not involve a lot of physicality, and that's okay! We are not all called to the same roles of strength and stamina. But what happens in your life when an opportunity comes along that is in more of a demanding setting? Do you let the opportunity pass you by because you're afraid of failure or you think it will be too hard? These questions are ones that reek of fear and unfaithfulness. God would never give you an opportunity that is too big for you. *"No temptation has overtaken you except what is common to mankind. And God is faithful; he will not let you be tempted beyond what you can bear. But when you are tempted, he will also provide a way out so that you can endure it"* (1 Corinthians 10:13).

Our God is so good that He knows exactly what you can handle. So think on this, what if God gives you an opportunity to go somewhere or do something physically challenging? He has given it to you; that's no mistake. You are the right person for this task. Will you endure the hardship for Him, or will your lack of physical fitness make you fearful and reject the opportunity? Your body is an instrument God can use to love and serve others, but will you decide to not love others because your body may not be able? I'm not talking about always doing the "heavy lifting" to love on others because not all of us are able to, but we can still serve in several ways by making our bodies usable for God.

I remember back to a time when I was running track in high school. My coach decided to make me a part of the 4×4 relay race. The 4×4 is a race with four people that all run one full lap after the other, which is 400 meters. Ask any track athlete; it's a grueling race. I actually despised that race because it was so hard, even though I was decent at it. I always pleaded with my track coach to put me on another relay team, but he stuck me to it. Of course, this awful race was always the last relay race of the day. The race always made me dread an entire track meet because I knew what lay in wait for me at the end: burning lungs, muscles on fire, and an endless search to find the stamina to push harder. One time at a meet, I thought so long and hard about the ending results of the race I made myself feel sick. Then I realized if I felt ill enough, then I wouldn't have to run the race. I kept thinking of the race and kept making myself feel even worse to the point of almost throwing up. Finally, I convinced my coach I couldn't run it, so he found a substitute for me. At first, I was overjoyed with the thought of skipping my race. But then something strange happened; I felt awful for abandoning my team. I made someone else endure a task they were not trained for and suffer the aftermath that would have been easier for me to endure. I realized that my selfishness and laziness not only cost me the trust of my teammates, but I missed an opportunity to grow.

Being physically able to go where God calls you is a little like my 4×4 race. It is never easy, and it will test us on what we're really made of. We can so easily get caught up in fear of the unknown and how bad it may hurt, but we can't let that stop us from running our race. What if your race is maintaining a certain degree of fitness so that you are able to serve in church wherever you are needed? Would you run the race of staying healthy so that in your later years, your family and your church are not prematurely burdened with your lack of health? Of course, certain things happen to us unexpectedly, like accidents or diseases. But if you're reading this book with a physically healthy body, then there is no excuse for you to say no to God for the race He has laid before you. If you do say no to God, He will find someone who is willing to run it for you, but you will miss out on that growing opportunity.

After my race, I was so ashamed of my lack of performance that I told my coach the truth and asked for his forgiveness. He wasn't pleased with me, but he allowed me to run the race for the rest of the season. Do you know what happened? Our 4×4 team made state. Boy was I glad then that I had said yes to running my race. I had a new reason to run, and it was to honor God with my performance, no matter how hard it was or how much I disliked it. Before every race, I would write Philippians 4:13 on my hand so I could read it right before. "I can do all things through Christ who strengtheneth me." I knew that I couldn't run my race no matter how much I trained, but I could trust God to get me through the race. So today, will you trust God to prepare you to run whatever race you are tasked with? Will you rely on His strength to get you through that opportunity, and will you be willing to let your body be usable by God?

Training for This Life and the Next

I would like to talk about my all-time hero that I've looked up to since I was a kid, Tim Tebow. For those of you who don't know who he is, he is one of the few Christian athletes that made God his goal while using his sport as the platform. He started out playing football for the Broncos (who just so happened to be my home team in Colorado). I actually really didn't like watching football growing up, as I would have rather just gone outside and played myself. It wasn't very exciting to watch, in my opinion, because none of the players meant much to me, but my dad and brother always had some game or two playing, and occasionally, I would find myself watching. However, there was something about just sitting down and watching the game for a couple of hours that just drove me nuts. Ask any of my family members, and they would tell you that I don't sit well at all, no matter what we're doing, to begin with. Anyways, one time when I found myself watching, I found this one football player fascinating, Tebow. When he made touchdowns, he would kneel and point his finger to the sky. This action was eventually pinned as "The Tebow." It was his way to give all the glory to God for his performances. I was completely taken aback by this guy. Here he was, a young, athletic man that wasn't afraid to show his faith in the game he loved. I was inspired from head to toe to be like him. Of course, my family would tease me that I only liked him due to his looks. Don't get me wrong, he's an attractive guy, and I was in high school, so you can put those two together. Glad it didn't work out because, no offense, Mr. Tebow, but my husband's the best. But besides that fact, I was truly attracted to how he showed the world that God was the Lord of his life in sports. Man, I wanted nothing more than an ounce of his confidence and bravery to do that in my sporting life. I started to read more about him to find what made him click. When he came out with his first book, I bought that thing as fast as I could and started to dig in. Let me tell you, his book spoke right to my heart. From athlete to athlete, he pointed out ways I could grow in my faith, how to serve God through my sports, and how to become who God meant for me to be. Gosh, I get excited now just remembering that feeling I had reading his book! It's like someone finally understood me for me; he got what I was struggling with as a Christian in the sports world.

It wasn't until college that I realized Tebow's wisdom was not only applicable in my sporting life but hugely important in my journey with taking care of my body. He talked about work ethic, dedication, honesty, and honoring God with how I achieved fitness. What I really loved was his consistent theme of being a tool used to reach others through his fitness. I believe this is a huge part of the ministry we can have on others, whether it is through sports, physical activities, church, small groups, and more. *"And whatsoever ye do in word or deed, do all in the name of the Lord Jesus, giving thanks to God and the Father by him"* (Colossians 3:17). In whatever we do, we are called to do this in the name of Jesus. I know in my heart that when

God was using Tim Tebow's message to talk to me, He was telling me how important it is to use our bodies for this life and the next. Maintaining and preserving ourselves for this life will take hard work and sacrifice, but more than that, it can be a living testimony to others. Let me share with you one of my favorite sections from Tim Tebow's book *This Is the Day* (pgs. 122–125):

Be the Example Others Will Follow

When I was a sophomore, I transferred to Nease High School to play football. New to the team, I had quite an impression to make. I wanted to prove I was the best. I also wanted to change the culture of a team that was known for being every-one's homecoming game. I wanted to be the example of what it meant to have heart, character, and fight.

Near the end of my first season with the team, we faced off against Pedro Menendez High School. At the end of the first quarter, we were already getting demolished, 17–0. After I was throwing on the run, I planted my right foot underneath me and one of the defenders hit me low. I heard a sickening crunch. My right leg snapped. Red-hot pain surged through me as I hobbled to the sideline. Coach Craig Howard asked if I was alright.

"Yeah, I'm fine," I replied, blinking to try and clear the haze of pain.

"Well, good. 'Cause we've got a game to win. Son, we're down seventeen to nothing. This is the stuff legends are made out of.

Now get back in there!"

I jogged back on the field and fought hard, trying to compensate with my good leg for the bum one. The limp I was playing with got worse with every passing quarter. Whenever the pain would start to compromise my game, I'd remember Coach Howard's words: "This is the stuff legends are made out of."

It wasn't about winning the game. It was about my teammates. It was about the team. It was about trying to change our reputation of being soft. If I wanted to be a leader, I had to act like one. I had to build the respect of my teammates. I couldn't think of a better way to do that than to play on a broken leg.

I'll never forget at the end of the fourth quarter running twenty yards toward the end zone. A safety was gunning for me. He came in from an angle, and his angle met mine on the one-yard line to the tune of a nasty collison. I got the touchdown, but he broke his leg. On a high note-for our team, at least-Nease evened the score 24–24.

When Menendez won the game 27–24 with a winning field goal, my heart sank. I remember limping toward my parents on the sideline. I hurt so bad, I could barely stand. Knowing there was only one more game in the season and I wouldn't be able to play due to my broken leg, I cried.

The worst thing about getting injured is not necessarily the pain of the injury but the pain of what the injury will cost. It's the pain of what you will miss out on. The pain of wondering if someone is going to get a jump on you while you rehab. Yeah, I hurt. But the disappointment of not being able to play was worse. I was determined to come back stronger and faster after sitting out the rest of the season. You don't get a lot of moments in life to prove yourself, but in that game I was given that chance. It was the first time in ten years that the school had a break-even season. The next year was even better. More people wanted to try out for the team. More players bought into the mentality that working hard would pay off. More teammates showed up in the weight room. And in our senior year, we won our first-ever state championship.

If you want to create change and influence others, you need to earn their respect. You do this not only by loving them, treating them with kindness, and not being judgemental but also by being committed. By showing them what it means to give your all, not just with words but in action. Do more than just talk.

Ultimately, life is based on a bunch of choices. The most important decision you'll ever make is to say yes to trusting Jesus. Going forward, you must decide what to do with whatever He puts on your heart or asks of you. Maybe you feel nudged to take a mission trip. Or start a business. Or go back to school. Or take better care of your health. Or spend more time with your loved ones. When you are pursuing a desire you feel God has given you, it's important to put in the work.

Some people believe that you're either born with a solid work ethic or you're not. I believe it's based on choices. It's about making the choice to say yes to the right things over and over and over again. You may not feel like it. It might be hard. It might require some pain. But you do it, and you don't stop doing it.

Make up your mind to do whatever is before you as best as you can. Focus on these priorities, and don't get anxious about the result. You don't have to reach your goal or dream overnight. Actually, you probably won't.

And one last thing: don't get sidetracked if you experience a setback or stumble from time to time. It happens. It might happen again. Resolve to get up, take another swing, and keep at it.

If you haven't had the chance to read Tim Tebow's books, I highly would recommend you do so. Even if you're not an athlete, they will still encourage you. The wisdom and encouragement of serving the Lord just seep out of his books.

I want you to remember his words:

It wasn't about winning the game. It was about my teammates. It was about the team. It was about trying to change our reputation of being soft. If I wanted to be a leader, I had to act like one. I had to build the respect of my teammates...If you want to create change and influence others, you need to earn their respect. You do this not only by loving them, treating them with kindness, and not being judgemental but also by being com-

mitted. By showing them what it means to give your all, not just with words but in action. Do more than just talk.

Tebow is making a huge point here. We have been called to be leaders. All of us. Not everyone will get up on a podium like Martin Luther King Jr., but some of us will, and some of us will be leaders in our churches, small groups, everyday living. Did you pick up on that? We can be leaders in our everyday lives! This is what I've been trying to drive home to you. *"You don't get a lot of moments in life to prove yourself"* (paragraph 8). God has placed each and everyone one of you perfectly where you need to be. He is using you to train for this life and the next.

Do you want to be a leader that sits on the sidelines, limping with a broken leg (impairing fitness), or do you want to push past that and be the leader other Christians and non-Christians need to see today? How could your fitness journey inspire others? Think of men or women that you see constantly exercising either in your neighborhood or at the gym. Don't you admire how hard they work and what an inspiration they are to those around them? You see a dedication in them that isn't in most people and wonder where they get it. Imagine asking them, and they give all the glory to God for their abilities. They are being good stewards of what He's given them so they can give in return. That could be you! I'm not saying you have to go pound the weight like that mammoth of a man in your gym, but I am saying you could dedicate yourself to training your body for this life and the next to be that leader for others. When people see your dedication, they will want to know what is inside you that gives you strength. And I hope that you are able to stop and say, "God gives me all my strength. I'm only using what He gave me to serve Him better."

Today is the day to get up off the couch. To push through the pain of that broken leg (I hope you don't actually have to do that). Start building the respect of your fellow Christians and non-Christians. Start creating change by loving, treating them with kindness, not passing judgment, and being committed to the body God gave you. Tebow called it exactly right; we often don't get many chances to prove what we're really made of. But today, tomorrow, and for the rest of your life, you can change that. Start training your body so that when your "broken leg" moment comes, you are able to push past it to give all the glory to God.

Chapter 5

FINDING WISDOM IN FITNESS

I said to myself, "Come now, I will test you with pleasure to find out what is good." But that also proved to be meaningless. "Laughter," I said, "is madness. And what does pleasure accomplish?" I tried cheering myself with wine, and embracing folly-my mind still guiding me with wisdom. I wanted to see what was good for people to do under the heavens during the few days of their lives. I undertook great projects: I built houses for myself and planted vineyards. I made gardens and parks and planted all kinds of fruit trees in them. I made reservoirs to water groves of flourishing trees... I became greater by far than anyone in Jerusalem before me. In all this my wisdom stayed with me. I denied myself nothing my eyes desired; I refused my heart no pleasure. My heart took delight in all my labor, and this was the reward for all my toil. Yet when I surveyed all that my hands had done and what I had toiled to achieve, everything was meaningless, a chasing after the wind; nothing was gained under the sun...A person can do nothing better than to eat and drink and find satisfaction in their own toil. This too, I see, is from the hand of God, for without him, who can eat

or find enjoyment? To the person who pleases him, God gives wisdom, knowledge and happiness, but to the sinner he gives the task of gathering and storing up wealth to hand it over to the one who pleases God. This too is meaningless, a chasing after the wind.

Ecclesiastes 2:1–7, 9–11, 24–26

This section in Ecclesiastes is so very powerful. It is King Solomon explaining his journey, trying to see if this life could satisfy us. So many different ways he tried to satisfy that constant hunger. He made great buildings and luscious gardens. He strove to have the finer things in life. He sought after having food and drink to try to satisfy him. Everything he laid eyes on, he acquired. There was nothing he didn't have. Even though he had riches beyond compare, Solomon realized that all those things were meaningless. The things he did or obtained were just that, things. Realization dawned on Solomon as he found that only through God would a man be blessed with wisdom, knowledge, and happiness. All the things he sought after were fleshly desires, not God-given. Earthly things can never satisfy our thirst, but if we are filled with living water, then we shall never thirst again (John 4:14).

I want to make a parallel between Solomon's story and our physical life. Thankfully God knew we would need so many examples and stories that we could relate to. I'm so grateful He has led me to this biblical lesson today to share with you. Take a moment and be creative with me. Imagine all the things King Solomon sought after can compare to how we think of our bodies today.

1. The Buildings = Our Bodies

Think about what is required to make a building: dedication, lots of hard work, hours upon hours of grueling labor, sacrifice, investment of time and money. Now think about what people go through to get their "dream body:" Dedication, hard work, grueling training, sacrifice, investment of time, and more commonly, lots of money. People will put hours, weeks, months, and years of work into investing into their bodies. Sacrifice happens all the time because suddenly finishing this framing project of a perfect physique is more important than spending time with friends or family. We are convinced that once the project is done, our building will be the most beautiful, the most envious of them all. There's no denying the fact that the people who've gone down this road are putting in long hours, hard work, sweat, and time. But all those days spent investing are reaping no profit because they will never fill that hole in their heart. That skinny waist won't satisfy. The extra muscle and definition will be like cardboard, worthless for building an actual house. These people who seek these "buildings" will never achieve that happiness because they are not building for God; they are building for their own selfish desires. They are chasing after the wind.

2. Luscious Gardens = Our Appearance

I imagine Solomon tore, bruised, scraped, cut, and even bled to make luscious and beautiful gardens and vineyards. He toiled day after day to sculpt the most pleasing designs to produce the most delicious fruit. No matter how much he put into his gardens, they still couldn't satisfy. We live in an age now where it's normal to change your appearance. People tear and bruise their bodies because they hate what they see. We scrap, cut, and bleed by asking plastic surgeons to change our looks. Nose jobs, skinnier wastes, cheek lifts, or lip fillers. Some even go further to change their gender. We think that if we finally obtain those looks we've always desired, then we'll finally be happy. You know the worst thing about stuff like plastic surgery, botox, or just changing our appearances? It is never enough. This constant need for perfection doesn't end after the first, second, or third surgery. Makeup is not a dying industry either. People will buy more makeup to cover up the new flaw they see every day. Suddenly, it takes over and becomes an addiction. People will spend hundreds of thousands to transform themselves into the most beautiful or handsome individual. It has now become the new normal to change our appearances into what we've always wanted instead of being satisfied with what we were given. Appearance addiction is a vicious, unrelenting cycle. It will never stop; it will never be enough, and these people will never find the happiness they desire. Only God, our Maker and Creator of everything we live, breathe, and do, will fulfill us. He is the only way to find true happiness and contentment in ourselves.

3. *Food and Drink = An Unrelenting Hunger*

As Solomon filled his belly with fancy wine and decadent food, he realized that even he was using his food to be his contentment in his day. We see this thinking is very prominent in a lot of ways today. People are living their lives with the idea that working hard and trying to live life to the fullest while being a good person will bring them the satisfaction that they did a good job. We know the truth to be different, however. We need to stop this unrelenting hunger for something more. We need to realize that the true meaning of contentment in our life is impossible to live in light of eternity. It is time to stop seeking this world, hoping it will fill our bellies and make us happy. God will give wisdom, knowledge, and joy to a people that are good in His sight. But those who grasp after this of this world, trying to be content with only the work of their hands and what fills their bellies, will always be hungry.

With all of these things together, I want you to realize that if you want to start on a fitness journey, your heart has to be seeking after the wisdom and happiness God can give you. Don't seek after the things of this world that will never satisfy. Seek to serve God, and you will find contentment no matter what you do. Seek after God, and He will grant you wisdom in your actions.

Building Our Buildings—Right or Wrong Reasons

Since we're talking about wisdom, let's talk about an area in health and fitness that seems to lack quite a bit of wisdom.

"Do not be conformed to this world, but be transformed by the renewal of your mind, that by testing you may discern what is the will of God, what is good and acceptable and perfect" (Romans 12:2).

We've seen this verse a couple of times in this book already. Maybe it's starting to be a theme that we are too earnestly conforming to this world. Absolutely! It's how we dress, act, talk, try to be a part of the "in" crowd. The cool people wear those clothes, so why shouldn't I? That guy looks really good when he wears his tight shirts like that, so I want to as well. Man, that girl at the gym got a lot of attention with those leggings. I'm going to get them on Amazon right now!

Oh, bother, did that ring a bell? It should have! We all are constantly wanting what others have and usually will do close to anything to achieve it. *"But I say to you that everyone who looks at a woman with lustful intent has already committed adultery with her in his heart"* (Matthew 5:28). This verse is talking about the fact that when someone looks at another with lustful or wanting eyes, they have already committed adultery with that person in their heart. Whether you want to be upfront right now or not, I'm going to point out some common areas in the fitness world where all are tempted and maybe even guilty, according to Matthew 5:28.

Clothing: What is the normal attire at your gym or place of fitness? Let me just take a few guesses: tight muscle shirts, compression pants, yoga pants/leggings, tight-fitting tops or low cut tops or crop tops, sports bra and no shirt, or maybe just lack of clothing entirely. Have I guessed a couple? I would be willing to bet that you have seen someone wearing something like I suggested. Why? Because that attire is the new normal, the cool clothes, the official "I'm serious about fitness, so this is what I wear" now clothes.

First off, health and fitness should never be made about the type of clothes you do or don't wear. Fitting into a tight sports top with leggings does not make you the fittest girl out there. It does, however, make you eye candy, but not for the right reasons. Wake up, ladies! We are no longer putting on these clothes because they "are comfy and fit better." No, if you would be honest with yourself, you'd be explaining how these clothes make you feel and how you hope it'll catch someone's eyes. Don't believe me? Fine, then I want you to try wearing a simple T-shirt and modest shorts to the gym. Do you feel quite as confident then, or do you wish you could scuttle right back to those leggings to feel "sexy" again?

Don't think you're off the hook either, guys. These new trends of muscle shirts and low-cut tanks that, if we're being honest, don't even count as clothing. Those compression pants that are not being worn with shorts over them. I can't tell you how many numerous times I've had to have conversations with the ceiling in the gym to avoid those unpleasant pants.

Oh sure, some of you are saying, "Well, just don't look at it then if it'll make you think something bad." That's not how our flesh works! If I recall correctly, Adam and Eve brought sin into the world that would haunt us and forever be our downfall until the day we die. Thankfully, God knew we'd need a pardon, a way out from our sin, so He sent His Son to wipe our slates clean. Yes, this includes lusts of the flesh, thank the Lord.

Do you hear what I'm trying to say? Even if I try my hardest not to look at someone that is wearing something immodest and dangerous, my flesh will always get the better of me. I don't want to admit that it is something I can struggle with, but in all honesty, we all struggle with it. We will never get past this source of sin if we don't confess it.

My pastor just gave a wonderful message on forgiveness. He spoke out of 1 John 1:1 about how God is a forgiving God, but we have to admit our faults if we are to truly confess and repent of our sin. His main points were these: (1) acknowledge the fact of your sin, (2) admit the fault of your sin, and lastly (3) accept the forgiveness of your sin. You want to start honoring the Lord the right way with health and fitness? You need to acknowledge, admit, and accept that we all sin in this area. I know I don't want to be a source of sin for others. I want to be healthy and live well, but not at the price that someone else has to live with lust in their heart. Is that what you want when you put on your gym clothes for the day?

Most of us don't even realize what we're doing now because this world has normalized the "fit" type of clothing that makes us think it's okay. Well, let's take a minute to think this through:

» You put on this new crop top and tight leggings that you just bought and hock them clear up to your shoulders (you know what I'm talking about, ladies), and your clothing choice for the day that makes you feel so confident and sexy. It will surely bring a man's eyes to wander and thoughts that lead him to sin.

» Guys, you put on a tight muscle shirt with no sleeves or maybe one of those threads-of-a-shirt that barely covers your chest. How does that little gal you've been eyeing avoid looking at you and not thinking something lustful?

Come on, people. I'm only pointing out a few clothing choices that bring the wrong kind of attention. I'm not trying to be a judge here; you wear what you wear. However, we are called to wear clothing that honors God, not the other way around. We are not being wise with how we dress at the gym or wherever we work out. Here's a saying my mother would coin when we girls would struggle if an outfit was appropriate to wear or not: "If you couldn't wear it around your family or church family, then the clothes probably are not very modest." Now I'm not saying you need to dress like a slug to workout. I'm saying that we need to be mindful of how we wear our clothes, what our intentions are by wearing the clothes, and prevent someone from committing a sin because of us. There are plenty of ways to dress modestly, cute, or masculine so that you can exercise with confidence. Seek wisdom today and dress for the right reasons when you are active.

How we act: I also want to touch how we act in or outside the gym. I want to call you out for how you behave in and out of the gym. It probably sounds a little harsh, but I don't think niceties are going to start waking people up from the sinful fitness atmosphere we've created.

When you go work out, do you do it for yourself, for God, or do you hope that someone could be watching? When you lift that heavy weight or run that distance, do you secretly deep down hope that someone was inwardly in awe of your stamina and strength? Maybe your little heart flutters when you see that big guy walking around you and notice he was watching you do your squats? Maybe you stretch to cool down in a "convenient area" that is very noticeable.

Let me tell you a story. When my husband and I first moved to Florida and were stationed at Eglin Air Force Base, we first started using the gym on base. I was really intimidated to go work out at the base gym because it was usually stuffed full and crawling with big, military guys. I've spent my fair time in gyms that always have a lot of men running around. However, I was still very uncomfortable, so I made my way to the further corner of the gym to work out as privately as I could. Once I finished lifting, I went to a small section of turf to stretch and cool down. As I was stretching, I noticed two girls came over to the same area to stretch as well. Both of these girls were young and very pretty. They both wore very tight leggings and skimpy shirts. This doesn't bother me at all, so I minded my own business. Shortly after, however, I felt like the gym was awkwardly quiet. I felt like there were tons of eyes suddenly in my area. The two girls were doing some rather "interesting" stretches were everywhere they turned, let's just say their posteriors were always visible to a crowd. With the tight leggings and the stretches, they were suddenly putting on a show. It wasn't the girls' stretching that bothered me. What bothered me was I looked up and realized that every pair of male eyes were watching the girls' every move. It was so obvious that most of the workout equipment was on pause as many stopped to watch. I feel like the girls had to have known they were quite the center of attention because their faces were lit up with the biggest smiles. Now, it's not my place to say what the girls' intentions really were or even judge them for their actions. That is something I pray is worked on in their own hearts. However, whether they purposely wanted attention or not, they certainly got it. And what's to boot is that there may have been many hearts that were led into temptation or sin.

What's the point of the story? I tell you about the girls because they're not the only ones who act that way in fitness settings. Actually, many of you probably have been a part of a "pause" moment when you see someone who stuns you, and not in a good way. When people dress provocatively, act provocatively, then the answer is obvious; they will attract sexual attention. Yep, that's right. That is basically the down and dirty of the fitness world today, sexual attraction. Uncomfortable yet? You should be because that's the honest truth, and we've let ourselves mindlessly ignore it for too long. There is only one way that can change, and it starts with the wisdom God has breathed in His Word on how to behave appropriately. The gym is not secular, apart from the Bible; it is absolutely included.

So how do we start changing how we act in the gym to be more like Christ-followers? The change actually starts right there, with the mindset to be a follower of Christ. If Christ is the center of your focus, the goal of your heart should be to honor Him however He has asked. So let me encourage you how to still be active and pursue fitness but to avoid some sinful traps laid before us:

» When you're working out, be mindful of who (especially what gender) is around you. Some exercises and stretches can attract attention. I'm not saying to not do the activity, but instead, wait until said person is gone or somewhere else. Reorganize your workout so that your activity that's a little more personal is able to be done at a time that's more appropriate. If it's unavoidable to change your workout organization or space it out with your present company, then consider finding a substitute exercise. I'm a personal trainer. I know there's more than one way to work a muscle, so trust me, you can find a different way if you have the desire to do it.

» When you are stretching, and this applies to men and women, try finding a wall to have your back to. Stretching is vitally important, and I always recommend it to all of my clients. However, you don't have to do it in the middle of everyone's eyesight for all to see. Instead, find a piece of equipment, a corner, or a wall to be next to. Basically, all I'm saying is be modest. It's easy to do all your stretches right next to objects so that you can still do your cooldown while modestly protecting personal areas of your body.

» When it comes to clothing, be mindful of what areas attract attention. Ladies, I'm not saying you can't wear cute outfits that look nice at the gym. I personally have never understood cute outfits when I just sweat in them anyways. But for those of you who like to dress up, that's okay. If you like leggings, consider finding a long shirt that can cover your backside. When you bend over to do an activity, is your shirt low enough to expose a certain area? If that's the case, then it's time to ditch the low cuts. No matter what you do in your workout, you will almost always have to bend over, and I promise you, it'll be just enough to let someone see something. There are many cute tops to be worn that are high neck, modestly cut, or there are those wonderful T-shirts again. Guys, a lot of clothing changes can be easy for you as well. Maybe dial back the tight-fitting shirts, wear your compression pants if it helps but cover with some shorts. It is easy and possible to dress modestly while working out.

Luscious Gardens—Sometimes the Answer Is No

When in Ecclesiastes 2, we get the very real picture that King Solomon paints for us about the beautiful vineyards and gardens he slaved over. He put so much time and effort into the gardens, yet when he was finished, he still wasn't satisfied. No work he could do would fill that hole in his heart. Only God could be the fulfillment in Solomon's heart, nothing else.

I think back to how sometimes in our own lives, God says no so that we turn towards Him. Back in my freshman year of high school, I was getting very competitive in volleyball. I had been placed as a libero on my team. For the many that may not know, liberos are the little people with the different colored jerseys that stay in the back row for defense. At first, I was so annoyed that I was permanently stuck in the back row, where nothing exciting happened. I wanted to be an outside hitter, and I had the power, just not the height. The front row was a cool and exciting place to be. Everyone cheered when a hitter pounded a ball or blocked another hitter. They were constantly getting the points for the game, whereas I saw myself totally sectioned off.

I remember at first I was angry that God would put me as a libero. For so long, I had pursued playing competitively, and now that I was there, He put me in the back row? My attitude was obvious on the court. I didn't want to be there, and it showed. Thankfully, I had a really good coach take me aside and show me what being a Libero really meant.

Libero—the rearmost roaming defensive player in volleyball. That is the basic definition of what I did in high school. However, I like this definition better: "Defensive specialist. Designed to add excitement to the game and raise the level of play!" I had never thought of a libero being a "defensive specialist." But the more I thought about it, the more I realized it was such a unique position, and there was only one on every team. Out of six players, I was the only defensive specialist, the only libero. I suddenly became so invested as a libero that I sought out to be the best libero I could be.

As the summers came and went, I attended numerous training camps and clubs to grow in my experience. During high school ball, I became confident, and the team voted me in as team leader. I remember feeling that sudden epiphany that libero was once a position I despised, but now it was a position I was utterly in love with. Come my junior year, I was made the top libero for our varsity team. Then in my senior year, for the first time in twenty years, our team made state. Volleyball challenged me in more ways than I ever would have imagined. I grew as a leader, a teammate, a friend, and I grew in my faith in God. He knew exactly what I needed to succeed, and it all started with Him saying no.

Have you been told no by God? I think we are told no several times in our life because we don't know what we need, but thankfully, God does. The same thing applies to building our bodies for Christ. We get so focused on our appearance that we think reaching our goals will make us happy. However, God is a bigger God than our goals. Sometimes with sports, we never reach our goals. For example, my senior team went to state but never placed. I had a learning opportunity that grew me more than winning state would have ever given me. Maybe you've set your dream fitness level on a pedestal but haven't been able to reach it. Have you ever thought that maybe it's because you're too focused on building a "luscious garden" instead of a body to be used by God? When we finally surrender our goals to God, He will put us at the exact fitness level we need to be at for His glory.

Maybe "no" looks a little different for you with your health and fitness. Perhaps, your "no" has been not being able to play sports, or your desire to be motivated and active has never been obtainable. I know God also uses people in those situations because, too often, we will rely on our own physical bodies to give us the reason to succeed. Actually, if we stop shooting for the moon and just tell God of our struggles, He will give us the strength we need to accomplish His goal. But it all starts right there in your heart. A willingness to surrender your goals, your "luscious garden" plans so that God can take first place in your life to fulfill you.

I think you'd be surprised how little goals and aspirations can be when you discover they're not God's, although, I pray, dear brothers and sisters, that you can lay down garden-working tools and decide to submit to God. And I pray you are filled with wisdom, kindness, and joy.

Unrelenting Hunger—What Do You Crave?

When King Solomon talked about all the amazing food he ate, he stated that it never satisfied him. The only satisfaction he eventually found was when he satisfied his soul with God. Earlier, we talked about how this world thinks that working hard and enjoying life is what fills you by the end of the day. But we know that God's Word tells us to not conform to the world. In fact, in 2 Peter 1 (verses 5–9), Peter is talking about how Christians should live for God:

> *To achieve this, you will need to add virtue to your faith, and then knowledge to your virtue; to knowledge, add discipline; to discipline, add endurance; to endurance, add godliness; to godliness, add affection for others as sisters and brothers; and to affection, at last, add love. For if you possess these traits and multiply them, then you will never be ineffective or unproductive in your relationship with our Lord Jesus the Anointed; but if you don't have these qualities, then you will be nearsighted and blind, forgetting that your past sins have been washed away.*

This powerful passage really hits home, as it charges how we are to live and thus be fruitful. But if we don't live after those qualities, then our lives will be barren and unfruitful, and we will continue to live as someone unsaved. We can never be truly filled if we live this life for ourselves.

So as we now look at the wisdom of how we pursue fitness, what is it that you crave in life? I don't mean a legitimate meal, but what is something you hunger after? Is it recognition, success, pleasure, or riches? We all strive after something, but the Bible tells us we should hunger after Him. *"A Psalm of David, when he was in the wilderness of Judah. O God, you are my God; earnestly I seek you; my soul thirsts for you; my flesh faints for you, as in a dry and weary land where there is no water"* (Psalm 63:1).

When you work out, do you ever think about how many other people are hungry but haven't found anything that satisfies? Maybe it surprises you to think about the people in the gym that way. Have you ever stopped someone you see every day and tried to give them friendly encouragement? What about that gym friend you have? Have you ever thought about inviting him or her to church? Here's the thing, in the fitness world, we have a powerful platform to reach others, yet most of us walk in and out of that gym (or whatever you go) every day and don't give people a second thought. Here we are, in a place where millions of people go and are hungry yet are never being fed.

Yes, we've discussed how we act and dress can be a testimony for our beliefs. But brothers and sisters, I'm challenging you now to think about being a light. I challenge you to think about reaching out to the hearts right around you. Reaching others should be our true goal of fitness, no matter what our physical desires may be. That hunger we strive for and have found with God should be our goal to share with others.

You are the light of the world. A city set on a hill cannot be hidden. Nor do people light a lamp and put it under a basket, but on a stand, and it gives light to all in the house. In the same way, let your light shine before others, so that they may see your good works and give glory to your Father who is in heaven.

Matthew 5:14–16

You have an opportunity to be a light in a very dark place, where sin runs ramped. Gyms, recreation centers, outdoor fields, and all the like all have people who are struggling with sin in their lives. And here you are, an available light in the darkness. You have the unique opportunity to be around the same people three, four, five, or even more days a week. That's just as consistent as a coworker, a friend, and family. Yet we don't really see our place of exercise as a godly platform. But that can all change today. I'm not asking you to start down a road of ministering; not all of us are called to preach. We all have our own special talents and abilities God has specifically given each of us. All of us have a part to play in someone's life, whether it be a smile, a handshake, or a friendly hug, words of love and encouragement, support, and the list goes on. So whatever your passion may be, or whatever you feel lead in your heart, do so for Christ. Go out and use your talents to love others as we have been asked to.

I want you to sit down in a quiet place, only focusing on God. Ask

Him to fill your heart with goals, people that you can reach where you workout. Ask for wisdom on how to approach someone, and love on them. Even if you feel like there's no one, I promise you that God will show you the exact person you need to help. He will show you exactly how to love on them. What an exciting way to look forward to exercising! That person you see every day may need a bright smile, encouragement on their work ethic, praise on their accomplishments. Trust me, the times someone has stopped me and given me encouragement make my day so much better. I always light up with a smile when I see them days after because I know they are rooting for me every day. Those people turn into my daily encouragers, a very present light in my grungy little gym. I don't know if those people are Christians, but even just their small actions mean so much. Imagine as a Christ-follower how you could impact someone's life.

So when you walk into your gym, your recreational center, your routine walking path with your dogs or children, make it a point to smile to someone. Reach out to that face you see every day and ask their name and how their day is going. Then make plans the next day and the next to reach out a little more. You might be surprised how quickly you'll form a friendship. What's even better, you'll be *amazed* how God can work people in your life to love on. Won't you make that your goal today?

Chapter 6

SEEING PAST FALSE PROMISES

In the presence of God and of Christ Jesus, who will judge the living and the dead, and in view of his appearing and his kingdom, I give you this charge: Preach the word; be prepared in season and out of season; correct, rebuke and encourage-with great patience and careful instruction. For the time will come when people will not put up with sound doctrine. Instead, to suit their own desires, they will gather around them a great number of teachers to say what their itching ears want to hear. They will turn their ears away from the truth and turn aside to myths. But you, keep your head in all situations, endure hardship, do the work of an evangelist, discharge all the duties of your ministry.

2 Timothy 4:1–5

Paul, the believed author of 2 Timothy, wrote this book when he was imprisoned. He knew his death was coming soon, but he knew he had *"…fought the good fight…finished the course…[and] kept the faith"* (2 Timothy 4:7). When he is writing one of his final letters, he is instructing Timothy that he must continue to serve faithfully even though it will be a hard and thankless task (verse 5). He challenges all to be on their guard as times will come when people will only want to do what they desire and will only listen to what they want to hear.

Nowadays, people want to listen to whatever music they want, different kinds of social media, politics, commercials, speakers, podcasts, and the list goes on. We turn off what is difficult to hear or what we think is meaningless. The same is true for people who hear a biblical message. Some people don't want to listen at all because then they would discover how their lives are truly filled with sin, and they would be convicted to change. I think the same goes for a lot of subjects in life we don't want to hear. Children don't want to be told what's good for them; teenagers don't want to be given direction; adults really dislike being told no or to wait.

Think back to the story of Jonah and the large fish. God told Jonah He wanted him to go down and speak to the people of Nineveh because sin was multiplying in the city. Jonah didn't want to speak to the Ninevites because they were enemies to him, and they were a dangerous people to be around. He knew God's wrath would come down on the city but wanted no part of it. As soon as he could, Jonah got on a ship to be far away from Nineveh. Shortly after, God delivered a horrible storm, and Jonah was thrown overboard to calm the sea. He was then swallowed by a giant fish and stayed there for three days and three nights. Once Jonah humbled himself before God, the fish spit him out. Then as he was commanded, Jonah went and preached to the Ninevites. The people of Nineveh believed what Jonah preached, turned, and repented from their sin, which saved them from God's wrath.

Isn't it amazing to think of what can happen if we listen to the right source? Jonah listened to his fear, his pride, and refused God. For his disobedience, he had to learn the hard way. Much like we have to learn in life today. Most of us refuse to listen to God, so we end up taking a much harder road. Through pain, suffering, and hardship, our pride is broken. God is the only one left to pick up the pieces.

In many ways in our daily lives, we refuse to hear what is good and instead open our ears to what the flesh wants. I like to think we behave along the same lines when it comes to healthy living. Think about diet advertisements. All of the advertisements out there promise weight loss in a short amount of time. "For just a small portion of money, you could lose this amazing amount of weight with no effort at all!" Does that sound familiar? How about workout programs? They are just as bad as diets. "See this amazing, built man that's in superb shape? He got it all by using the brand new… (insert new workout device), and it's so easy you can do it too!" I could wager that many of you have heard, seen, and maybe even bought into advertisements like those. We all have. Why? Because those advertisements are telling us exactly what we want to hear.

False Advertising

We want to be told that weight loss is easy. Losing pounds doesn't require any work, just spending a little money (which we always seem to justify the use of). People don't want to work hard or put time into something. Our generation is now lazy (resulting in many of the issues today) and only wants the path of least resistance.

I remember a girl I went to college with was so excited about this new fitness product she saw on TV. It was the "ab machine" that electrically contracted your abdominal muscles for you, and bam! Instant abs! She was so excited because all you had to do was stick the thing on your stomach every day, and eventually, you'd have a phenomenal six-pack. I tried to help my friend out by letting her know the ab machine would never work for her because it was just a scam. Nevertheless, she bought the machine. Sixty dollars and a couple of months later, my friend was fed up with the ab machine because she had noticed no difference. Just like that, she threw the contraption away and immediately started looking for a new and improved fitness item. I don't know if she ever reached her fitness goals, but if she did, I know it was not because of those get-rich-quick schemes.

That's the majority of the fitness industry today. It's a design, a program, a new "invented diet" that people sell, saying it will get you major results. The only major results you will see are less money in your wallet and another letdown in your fitness goals.

So why does the fitness industry sell things that don't actually help us get fit? I mean, isn't that why we have a fitness industry to begin with? That's the way things started, yes. People actually felt a desire to help others rebuild, recover, and grow stronger. It wasn't about the money, but then again, money is one of our fleshly downfalls. Quickly, the fitness industry started seeing how gullible the general population was to health-related products. Clients didn't care how they lost the weight, only that it worked. They realized that they could charge hundreds and hundreds of dollars for a ridiculously simple program, and people wouldn't bat an eye to buy it. People dive right in because they believe, with good advertising, that it will work. It's worth the money to go all in on this "magic" routine if it means they don't have to put in the work.

For example, think back to the most recent trainer you've seen pop up on social media or the TV. They are super trim, ripped, and for some reason, they usually are attractive. They tell you something along the lines of, "Wish you could have a body like this? Well, you can! Just check out my sixty-day training videos, and you will see the weight just melt off!" Insert this trainer, then hold a box of pizza, "You can even eat the foods that you want. Just follow my program and experience the new you today!" Ah, so typical. You can't scroll on your Facebook, Instagram, Twitter, or local TV station without seeing someone advertise the best way to lose weight for a certain amount of money.

Money! That's what almost any program is about! Trainers have found out how to hook people into what they're selling and make, you guessed it, hundreds and hundreds of dollars. Here's a secret for you that I have learned the hard way and from education. Every. Single. Program is the exact same thing. There's not a program out there that truly is the "new secret to weight loss." Someone didn't just stumble on the newest and greatest formula for how the body really needs to be trained for weight loss. If they had, it wouldn't just be your average, everyday trainer on your screen trying to pitch their program for you.

What really has happened is a trainer or exercise specialist has found a different way to construct a program, then labels it as the best workout program ever.

Take burgers, for example. How many restaurants out there brag that their burgers are the best? Did they actually enter a competition to find out? No, they all boast they have the best burger because that's what sells. You can have a mediocre burger at a joint but see that they're listed as the best burger in their county. Surprising, isn't it? Actually, it's not at all. That's how hundreds and hundreds of businesses sell any type of product around the world! Businesses bait the clients; the clients come in with high expectations, and the first burger they eat is actually pretty good! So one client tells a friend how good it is who passed it on to another friend. But after a couple of burgers, these clients realize that really that burger is just another burger. Just how a fitness plan or diet is really just another plan or diet.

So maybe now you're wondering what actually works then if all fitness advertisements can be bad? Well, let me tell you this first off. If you see an advertisement for something that seems too good to be true, it most definitely is. The truth about exercise programs is this: they take time, consistency, and correct application. Sandy's thirty-day ab-buster workout is not going to get you that six-pack. Jason's three-month booty-making boot camp is not going to get you that backside that you're wanting. But what about their followers that have been seeing results? The majority of those people not only followed the exercise plan but a strict meal plan as well so they can show *really good* results. They most likely had lots and lots of time to commit to just getting results, unlike so many of you that have actual lives to live.

The lies that the fitness industry sells frustrate me because I don't think it's fair to hide the honest inner workings of fitness just so they can make a couple of bucks. I have felt strongly that all fitness advice and legitimate programs shouldn't cost hundreds and hundreds of dollars. It's actually a large reason why I wrote this book. I wanted to share with you the simple, scientifically proven way to actually pursue an achievable healthy lifestyle. And believe me, it's not going to cost you an arm and a leg to figure it out. If you're dying to know how it all works, that information is all in the second section of this book.

Before you get too excited about the fitness section, I want you to remember some key items and the most important aspect of this book. First of all, please don't forget that yes, the aspects of fitness are important, but they will never outweigh the importance of serving God first. If you don't learn how to have the right heart for fitness, any health improvement you make will never be honoring to God. Secondly, there are many, many false teachers out there that just want your money. They don't really care if you lose weight, if you feel better, if you're able to reach your goals. Most programs want to use you and nothing else. So I want to encourage you; when your ears are inclined to listen to things that are too easy, that sound so perfect, air on the side of caution, instead of buying straight into their program, take a minute to research a couple of legitimate reviews. Try to find the articles or journals associated with the program. If there are no journals or articles, I'd run quickly in the opposite direction. If the article and journals are very vague and unclear, be hesitant to jump right in.

I'm not saying there is no good program out there. Thankfully there are trainers and exercise professionals that truly want to help without all the mumbo jumbo that has infested the rest of the industry. All I want you to learn is what Paul warned Timothy about. *"For the time will come when people will not put up with sound doctrine. Instead, to suit their own desires, they will gather around them a great number of teachers to say what their itching ears want to hear"* (2 Timothy 4:3–4). Paul is warning people about listening to false teachers that are trying to trick others in believing lies that have been twisted out of God's Word. I'm not trying to even begin to compare false teachers God has warned us about and bad fitness instructors. But I do believe God tells us to be vigilant with what we allow ourselves to hear. In the fitness industry, we have to be very vigilant.

Magic Diet = Magic Weight Loss?

I have to rein myself in to talk to you about dieting because if I let myself, I will write pages upon pages of my thoughts concerning diets. Now, are they another money-maker like the fitness programs? Absolutely! Do they actually work? Yes, in certain ways. But the big difference here in the, let's call it, the "diet industry" is that almost every program out there was based on a scientifically proven way to lose weight. That way is a reduction in calories.

"Oh, it can't be that simple. I've been following this diet for many months. I have to watch out for non-lean proteins, less starchy vegetables, no fruits, low fat, little dairy, etc., etc." This, my friends, are how legitimate diets are constructed. Diets are these miserable designs that cut out very specific foods, use crazy proportions, recommend very complicated supplements and oh-so-specific workout routines to follow. Diets are honestly miserable. Trust me, I've fallen prey to many, and there wasn't one that wasn't awful from start to finish. Oh sure, Sally over here will say that she's been doing keto for a couple of years, lost weight, and feels great. Well, I would like to ask Sally this, are you planning on doing keto until the day you die? No? Well, here's a shocker, when you finally get sick and tired of following the strict rules of no carbs, no sugars, only protein and fats, you will finally let your body regulate food normally again, and you will gain all that weight right back.

I have to tell you; there is no secret about Dr. Oz's newfound diet that will make you lose the weight you've always carried. All diets do the exact same thing; they reduce your calorie intake, which can make you lose weight. However, so few people stick to a diet for long periods of time because they get burned out from the rigorous demands, so they don't think that lifestyle is worth the results. There is no "magically newfound fruit" that they make into pills that is going to burn belly fat while you sit and do nothing. Those pills you spent $40 on? Yeah, they're basically placebos. Diets, pills, premade meals all do the exact same thing, make money.

Okay, if I'm such a smarty-pants about calling out all these different diets, then what diet do I suggest to lose weight or be healthy? Here's the secret, I never recommend a diet to anyone. I think of diets like this, D—Doing, I—Idiotic, E—Eating, T—Tricks. That's what they honestly are! Diets are put together with ridiculous rules and regulations that you pay someone else for so that you can put yourself through them. Now, sometimes people have to go through dietary restrictions because they can't eat certain foods like vegetarians, vegans, or paleo, for instance. However, I'm talking to the people that willingly put themselves through ridiculous diets to find results. Just Google "different types of diets," and you will be amazed how many hundreds of diets are out there. Just for fun, here are some of my top favorites: blood type diet, baby food diet, juice cleanses, the water diet, the vision diet (literally wearing blue lensed glasses to make food look less appealing), cabbage soup diet, apple cider vinegar diet, and the fist diet (eat anything as big as your fist). I'm not kidding; these are legitimate diets. But other diets are a little more sneaky and tempting. Maybe some of you have tried them, and that's okay! I think the people who have been out there and done that can learn even more efficiently about eating well.

I don't suggest diets, but I do recommend a healthy eating regimen. Isn't that the same thing as a diet, just with a different label? No. What I encourage are holistic-based habits that you learn slowly over time so that you can be successful for the rest of your life. The problems most people struggle with when it comes to diets are expenses, nonrealistic, burnout, and, oh yeah, life happens.

What many diets don't like to explain is what you are supposed to do when Murphy's Law shows up and makes dieting almost impossible? Well, that's because these diets live in a perfect world where people have loads of time, money, dedication, and nothing bad ever happens. How is that practical for everyday life? Let me put it to you this way, how does the mom of three kids try to maintain a demanding diet when she's running all kids to different schools, practices, planning and making meals, and maintaining her life? What happens when a kid calls out sick, but the other two still have school? She doesn't have time to stay away from starchy vegetables or low-carb foods. She is hungry, tired, and needs something to get her through the day. Boom, diet is done, and then the poor mom feels like a failure, so she just gives in to all her cravings and loses all her progress. Trust me; I'm not picking on this mom here. She's done nothing wrong; she's trying to live her life while being responsible for raising several others.

So what is the problem? The biggest issue is that no diet is catered around the average, busy lifestyle today. All diets try to hook you on the promise of losing weight quickly. If you have a limitless amount of money, your own schedule, then sure, a diet probably will fit your lifestyle just fine. But for the rest of us that have to work forty hours a week or more, have several children to take care of, businesses to run, these quick-fix diets just don't have what it takes to make it work.

In section two of this book, I go into great detail about how slowly adapting good eating habits can help you find your level of health more practically, life-friendly, and guilt-free. I don't believe God has lovingly given us a way to sustain ourselves just so that we can abuse it. I also don't believe we need to starve ourselves, abuse, and misuse our bodies with what we eat just so that we can lose weight.

I had to learn a lesson a little while ago about food. I treated all junk food as an idol. I adored it, couldn't get enough of it. It became a source of pride for how much I could eat of a certain item. Then it switched to where I wanted to lose weight, and suddenly, it became a different type of idol. I was obsessed with eating the perfect types of foods, how much, how little, and looked down on others who ate poorly. Eventually, I saw how this unhealthy relationship with food was making my body miserable; my heart was certainly in the wrong place, and it didn't prepare my body to be used for God. My heart had to get right with God first; then, I had to trust that He would take care of my body. I had to sit on my knees one night to ask for help to overcome this ridiculous but real dependence on food. Isn't it amazing that God already knew we would need help in that area?

> Then Jesus said to his disciples: "Therefore I tell you, do not worry about your life, what you will eat; or about your body, what you will wear. For life is more than food, and the body more than clothes. Consider the ravens: They do not sow or reap, they have no storeroom in the barn; yet God feeds them. And how much more valuable you are than birds! Who of you by worrying can add a single hour to your life? Since you cannot do this very little thing, why do you worry about the rest?"

> Luke 12:22–34

I absolutely love this passage. If I let myself, I will worry myself sick about anything. But thank God that He has been growing me to trust Him in whatever area of life instead of worrying. Even when it comes to what and how we eat, He is still telling us that we can trust in Him. Whether you would like to admit it or not, we all have let food and diets become our own idols. We worry constantly about food, and it's taken our focus away from our heavenly Father. I suppose it sounds a little silly to think something as simple as food can worry us so much we forget to trust God. Again, God knew we would struggle *"Since you cannot do this very little thing…"* He knows that we can't manage this life on our own, even down to how we eat and dress! That's why we have to trust Him in all aspects of our lives, not just the more obvious ones.

I want to encourage you today. It's time to stop letting food dominate your everyday life. It's time to instead trust God that He will provide for you the best way to take care of yourself, even the food you need. As you read into section two, you will learn how to grow your unhealthy habits into healthy ones. Habits that can be glorifying and healthy.

Chapter 7

HARD WORK MEANS HARD WORK

A sluggard's appetite is never filled, but the desires of the diligent are fully satisfied. The righteous hate what is false, but the wicked make themselves a stench and bring shame on themselves. Righteousness guards the person of integrity, but wickedness overthrows the sinner. One person pretends to be rich, yet has nothing; another pretends to be poor, yet has great wealth. A person's riches may ransom their life, but the poor cannot respond to threatening rebukes. The light of the righteous shines brightly, but the lamp of the wicked is snuffed out. Where there is strife, there is pride, but wisdom is found in those who take advice. Dishonest money dwindles away, but whoever gathers money little by little makes it grow.

Proverbs 13:4–11

King Solomon is our author of these Proverbs. He is giving us a much-needed lesson on a godly lifestyle. He presses on to explain how to live a godly life with honesty and that insomuch can bless us with worldly success. He particularly touches on a subject that is really important, the damaging effects of laziness.

Laziness leads to many things, but mainly disaster and sin. Our current generation really thrives on one thing, being oh so very lazy. I don't say that to be judgemental, but I say that with the observation that people nowadays don't want to have to work for a single thing; they want it all given to them.

Have you ever watched the animated movie *WALL-E*? If you haven't, I highly recommend it, as it is such a cute movie with a great story. To give you a quick outline, I can tell you that WALL-E is a clean-up robot on earth many, many years in the future. Humans took poor care of earth so that it is now so uninhabitable that everyone decides to get on ships that will let them live in space until they find a new planet. WALL-E, being a robot, doesn't think anything of the disappearance of the population because he continues to clean up the piles and piles of trash that humans left behind. As WALL-E's story builds, we find that he has a personality and longs to find companionship. He eventually finds another robot named EVE, and they fall in love. As the movie progresses, we finally get our look into the current human race. All of the humans that live on the lifeboats are horrendously overweight. None of them can walk, so they all have hovering machines to take them everywhere they go. There is always some type of food in their hands, made even more conveniently as a liquid so they can be on the go. All humans are so obsessed with their online friends, but they don't connect to the people physically around them. Does any of this seem oddly familiar to you yet?

As the story continues, WALL-E and EVE interrupt several lifestyles while trying to save everyone's lives. Some humans, for the first time in a long time, start to make connections with other people around them. Basically, people are woken up from the virtual world they lived in. Further down the story, when push comes to shove, they have to learn how to walk all over again like giant oversized babies. Through WALL-E and EVE's triumph, they overcome the obstacles and find a new place to live. Once on their new planet, people start to work again. Planting fields, growing crops, and providing for one another. Soon you cut to the end of the movie that is much further in the future, and everyone is healthy again. Kids are running and playing. Adults are working and being a part of families. And WALL-E and EVE have their happily ever after.

Healthy Lifestyles Don't Magically Happen

I remember when I first watched *WALL-E* with my family, and my parents said it was a spot-on representation of what people will eventually become if we keep going down the drain like we are. My parents weren't trying to be facetious; they were being realistic. To give you some perspective, I can tell you my mom has been a nurse for over thirty years. She's seen the ups and downs of healthcare over the years and how people's health has gone from bad to worse. My father was a volunteer firefighter who saw some of the worst situations people were in. I think they had some good insight to an upcoming problem.

Now, as an adult, I truly am starting to understand the meaning of the phrase, "You will understand when you're older." The lessons my mother and father taught us kids about taking care of ourselves and future families were and are still so valuable. They made sure to keep us kids healthy and active, and now I'm so grateful they instilled that in us.

You see, when it comes to people's health, today we are so lacking in the effort put in that now we don't know how to take care of ourselves. We've talked about the new fitness and diet trends that hook people into their schemes as it promises to be a quick fix. However, we haven't talked about the realistic side of how to obtain a healthy lifestyle.

Bottom line, healthy lifestyles are not obtained overnight. They must be earned by education, growth, hard work, and consistency. It is so possible for anyone in whatever state to begin adapting oneself to a healthier lifestyle. But for many, the dedication that it takes to adhere to a better lifestyle seems impossible, and that's why a majority of people want the easiest route. Let me tell you this; you will have to put in some work to improve your lifestyle. But that does not mean it will be an arduous, painful journey. What can ruin your life is you continuing to let your body go down the unhealthy road to a faster morbidity. Oh, was that a little dark? Good! I'm not trying to fluff up the situation for you and make you think everything is fine and dandy. The truth is that for too long, people have been trying to be "nice" about current lifestyle habits, so now nobody is taking the possible outcomes seriously.

Remember a couple of chapters back, I shared the statistics of obesity becoming a major disease? Well, what's even worse is now it's considered an epidemic. It is such a scary and rising epidemic in the US that currently, it is causing over 300,000 deaths per year. That number is not including those who are overweight that are diabetic, have hypertension, or are at risk for stroke. So let me ask you this, would you rather put in some hard work to improve your quality of life and your family's, or do you want to take the easy road and let yourself go down a very unhappy and dangerous road that could even eventually kill you?

Now since that subject is out in the light, let me take time to now encourage you. Your life is what you make of it. God has placed you on this earth for a reason and for a certain amount of time. We all only have so much time to do the work the Lord has placed on us before we are called home. "*Teach us to number our days, that we may gain a heart of wisdom*" (Psalm 90:12). There's that fickle word again, "wisdom." If we are to be wise people, we should take the initiative to take care of what we are given, our bodies. Yes, it will take some work on your part. But what I want to teach you is that it's not a scary or impossible road. All you need is an attitude for change, a heart that's right with God, and a will to put your best foot forward. If you have those traits today, you're already putting in the work to improve your life.

Dedication and Hard Work at Whatever Stage

I mentioned before that my dad was a volunteer firefighter. He learned a lot of valuable lessons about people that he passed on to us kids over the years. One of the biggest things I will always remember is that he told us to never be like sheep and follow a herd. What he meant was that people tend to do what others do without even thinking.

If you don't know much about sheep, the biggest thing to learn is that whatever one does, all will follow. So if one sheep jumps off a cliff, the rest will mindlessly do the same thing. Sheep are not known for being smart or independent animals. After showing them in 4-H having to raise and take care of them, I can understand why they tend to be "not as smart as others" in the animal kingdom.

My dad always used sheep as an example because he and my mom believed that not enough people try to think for themselves. I agree. Just look at social media. We all want what a popular person has. We try to copy them in even the smallest ways like clothing, hair, speech, style, etc. When you walk in a populated place but don't know anybody, what do you automatically do? Pull your phone out and try to look busy. Well, if you look up from your phone, you'll notice that almost every single person around you is doing the exact same thing.

So why is it important for me to make the point about being an individual? It's a huge area for me to show you because, in fitness, the goal of every trainer, diet, fitness equipment all try to get you to look the same! All avenues of health and fitness put every person in a box and assume it will be the right fit for each individual. Workouts can be for everyone; all diets are perfect for whoever; any fitness equipment will burn the fat off anyone. Again, we are starting to uncover how bad the industry has become.

No one is like the other in sense of personality, aspirations, talents, and abilities, and yes, even our physical bodies. We are all built differently and for a good reason. If we all were built like Barbie or G.I. Joe, then our lives would be so very limited and boring. Thank God that He has made us all different.

Different. That's what I want to get across to you right now. We all are at different stages of health in our lives. Our work ethic is different. Our everyday lives are different. Our current health and diagnosis are different than the person standing next to us. Everyone is unique with how their body acts and reacts to different areas of a physical lifestyle. *"But now, O Lord, you are our Father; we are the clay, and you are our potter; we are all the work of your hand"* (Isaiah 64:8). God has made each of us to be different from the other. With that being in mind, why would it make sense that we all should try to be at the same level as another? It doesn't! We shouldn't be trying to match anyone's current lifestyle because it's theirs, not ours.

When you start this road to a healthier lifestyle, I want you to quit comparing your work with someone else's. Stop thinking like a sheep, wanting to follow off that same cliff as another. Instead, start focusing on your own body only. Don't think about the fact that Shelly lost fifteen pounds in a month, and you've only lost five. Don't beat yourself up thinking, *What am I doing wrong? Why am I not seeing her results?* Her body is doing something different; she's different than you. Unless you are twins, do the exact same activities, interact with the same people emotionally, your life will never be comparable to another. So stop comparing someone's fitness journey with your own. What really matters is the dedication and hard work you put in at whatever stage and place in life you are at.

So today, I want you to sit down and think about who you are as a person: physically, emotionally, mentally, and all the above. Every single aspect of you comes into play when you start working on your health. Being able to understand where you struggle, thrive, lack confidence, and excel is so important. All areas are perfectly yours and need to be put into play when you decide to change your life.

Fruits of Your Labor

"Blessed is everyone who fears the LORD, who walks in his ways! You shall eat the fruit of the labor of your hands; you shall be blessed, and it shall be well with you" (Psalm 128:1–2).

This psalmist is giving us a lesson about how those who fear the Lord are blessed. If you walk in the ways the Lord has asked you to, you will prosper from the fruits of your labor. Notice how it doesn't mention how you will gain from the fruits of someone else's labor. Only yours. Our walk with God is a personal and individual one. Only by what we do will God bless us with fruitfulness.

"And hereby we do know that we know him, if we keep his commandments. He that saith, I know him, and keepeth not his commandments, is a liar, and the trust is not in him... He that saith he abideth in him ought himself also so to walk, even as he walked" (1 John 2:3–6).

Here we see another instruction to walk in the ways of Christ. In this passage, John is explaining the difference between those who truly know God and those who don't. Those who know Him should also build their relationship with Him by living their life for Him. But those who claim to know Him or don't know Him at all won't live lives that show they have a relationship with Jesus.

The point I'm wanting to drive home to you today is that we are called to follow after God. To live this life we have been given for His glory entirely. We are called to fear Him, love Him, and love others. By truly following after God, knowing Him, we will reap what we sow. We will eat the fruits of our labor.

Many of us, however, tend to be like the second example in 1 John 2:4, "*He that saith, I know him, and keepeth not his commandments, is a liar, and the trust is not in him.*" This type of attitude comes from a fleshly state of mind. We think we can strive after the world and get the benefits of being "religious" as well. Well, frankly, that type of lifestyle is one that God hates. "*I know your works: you are neither cold nor hot. Would that you were either cold or hot! So, because you are lukewarm, and neither hot nor cold, I will spit you out of my mouth*" (Revelation 3:15–16).

These powerful verses are talking about the dangerous Christian that is neither interested nor disinterested in serving the Lord. This is the most dangerous place a Christian can be because we cannot grow whether it is for good or bad. We are permanently stuck in between. You will never experience the fruits of your labor being lukewarm.

When you are called to be of service to God, you should be ready to follow wholeheartedly. Even if your service is volunteering at your church or donating your time at a local food bank, He expects us to follow Him with eager hearts. Maybe your service is something more simple, like spending time with an unsaved coworker or friend. Or maybe even you could serve God by taking care of your body.

So if God has asked you to start taking care of yourself and become a worthy living sacrifice, don't you think you should be willing to put the work in? Let's think about those who go to the gym five to six times a week and have what they like to call "massive gains." Sure, those guys and gals are so very muscular and fit, but their "labor" has all been in vain. They are like examples two and three in 1 John 2:3–4. Their labor will not produce any fruit if it's not for the cause of Christ. However, let's say you start putting in the work with the mindset of serving Christ. He will let you enjoy the fruits of your labor because you have done so for His glory.

I want to share a story about a remarkable athlete who really gave his life completely to follow after Jesus. Even though his story is one that ends differently than you might expect, I believe he experienced the fruit of his labor.

Eric Liddell, the star of the movie *Chariots of Fire,* was known as the "Flying Scotsman," who was an incredible runner in the Olympics. His faith, however, was bigger than any medal. For the 1924 Paris Olympics, Liddell refused to run in a qualifying heat because it was scheduled on a Sunday. Liddell was convicted of not running on the Lord's Day. However, he still ran in the four hundred meters and broke the world record. The 400 meters wasn't even his best race.

After the Olympics, Eric felt called to be a missionary in China. His wife and two daughters also lived with him for a time. Soon after, Japanese occupation in China made life very dangerous, and Liddell sent his family to Canada. Shortly after, the Japanese captured Liddell and placed him in a prison camp. The camp wasn't anything fancy, no running water or working bathrooms. He remained in that camp until his death at age forty-three.

Stories have since infiltrated from the other surviving prisoners of the camp to talk about "Uncle Eric." He was known as the kindest, most loving man who made the camp a home for others. He was a referee for children's games; he took care of the sick and weak and led Bible studies to teach others the Word. Liddell lived his life to serve Jesus, and it showed in every aspect of his life.

Parts of me wish I could take just an ounce of Eric Liddell's dedication to serving the Lord to use in my own life. But using the work and dedication he put in to serve would be pointless; it wasn't my race to run; it was Liddell's. Sometimes I think that's how we view ourselves today. We see these great men and women of faith and wish we could be like them or have the same attributes they do. If we did, then we could be successful and serve like they did or do. I believe that's where we try to "use someone else's fruit." There's a reason why the Lord said that we would grow from the *"fruits of our labor."* Ours. Not someone else's but ours alone. Someone else's work won't benefit us in any way. Great people can be a wonderful example to us, but in the end, it's on us. God has given each of us an individual life, individual talents and abilities, and an individual path. We can be put together with others to grow and love each other, but ultimately, the race is our own to run.

In the movie, *Chariots of Fire,* Eric's character speaks a phrase that I think we all need to hear today, "God…made me fast. And when I run, I feel His pleasure." Is there an area of your life that you could do for God and feel His pleasure? I know that when I'm truly serving God where He has asked me, I feel His love towards me. I know that I am honoring Him with my race.

It may not be your best race or even one you're good at, but I believe we are all called to run a race of healthy biblical lifestyles. I don't expect everyone to be Olympic runners, but I believe you need to perform your best to produce the fruit of your labor.

He Wants You to Be Useable, Why Don't You?

As for you, you were dead in your transgressions and sins, in which you used to live when you followed the ways of this world and of the ruler of the kingdom of the air, the spirit who is now at work in those who are disobedient. All of us also lived among them at one time, gratifying the cravings of our flesh and following its desires and thoughts. Like the rest, we were by nature deserving of wrath. But because of his great love for us, God, who is rich in mercy, made us alive with Christ even when we were dead in transgressions-it is by grace you have been saved. And God raised us up with Christ and seated us with him in the heavenly realms in Christ Jesus, in order that in the coming ages he might show the incomparable riches of his grace, expressed in his kindness to us in Christ Jesus. For it is by grace you have been saved, through faith-and this is not from yourselves, it is the gifts of God-not by works, so that no one can boast. For we are God's handiwork, created in Christ Jesus to do good works, which God prepared in advance for us to do.

Ephesians 2:1–10

116

When you read this passage, does your heart take a breath of relief knowing that even though you deserved pain, suffering, and a horrible death, our Father in heaven sent Jesus to make you alive again? When I was wondering what passage to attach to this subject, I fell upon this verse, and my heart just leaped for joy. I was so thankful to be reminded that there's no great deed I could do, no special act or perfect speech I could give; all I had to give was my heart in faith to be made alive again. Do you have that same joy today in you? I pray that you do, and know that it's no accident that you are where you are today. God has planned everything out for you perfectly, even to read this book. Why? For some reason, God knows you need what this book has to offer. Let me be clear; you do not need what I have to say; you need what God is saying through me to get to you.

At the end of this strong passage in Ephesians, there's a particular verse that really hits hard. *"For we are God's handiwork created in Christ Jesus to do good works, which God prepared in advance for us to do"* (verse 10). God created you, saved you from death, and now has a special purpose for your life. He has *"prepared in advance"* for us to do good works for His glory. God knows you inside out, and He knows what tasks to give you in your life to be able to do His will. He also created you and your body perfectly to be able to do His will. To do His will, we must be prepared, and to be equipped to do whatever task it may be, I believe God has asked us to ready our bodies for Him.

That's right, the better we take care of ourselves, the more we stay physically healthy, the more supplied we can be for this life. The better your health, the more energy you will have to serve His kingdom.

117

So if we see here that we are to be used by God to do His Will, what is stopping you from wanting to be healthy to serve Him?

Maybe some of you have the attitude that "God *can do anything*, so I shouldn't have to exercise or eat right. He will use me in whatever state I am in." Well, one thing is true, God can do anything, but this type of thinking is dangerous because you are giving God an ultimatum. "*Do not be deceived: God cannot be mocked. A man reaps what he sows*" (Galatians 6:7). You are putting yourself on a pedestal, wanting to tempt God to take your bait. To use you no matter your battered state. Let me ask you this, why would God want to use you, a broken-down, physically inept person that is daring Him to "perform a miracle" when somewhere out there, there's a person with their heart so on fire for the Lord he or she will do whatever they can to please Him? With this type of thinking, you are making yourself your own god by expecting God to serve you.

So what is it really that's holding you back from making yourself an available tool for the kingdom? Is it apprehension of the unknown? Do you fear that it will be really hard? Do you find a scapegoat saying you'll never have enough time or resources to make it possible? I'll be honest, all of those excuses are all *lies*. Those lies are told to you by none other than the devil himself. Yes, I said it, the devil is deceiving you into thinking you could never be physically healthy to serve God. Why? Just think about it, why would he want anyone to be the best versions of themselves to serve God? His total purpose is for us to tuck our tails and run away from anything having to serve God. Yes, even your health is a way for him to make you avoid God.

118

"The world would love you as one of its own if you belonged to it, but you are no longer part of the world. I chose you to come out of the world, so it hates you" (John 15:19).

Don't you see? This world so badly wants us to fall into the fleshly traps of doubt, lust, fear, and greed when it comes to our health. The world hates those who take a stand for Christ instead of going down the typical roads of physical health. All those lies you hear day and night about your body, your health, your physical well-being are a trap from the evil one of this world. You stop and look into a mirror, and all you hear is a voice of disgust talking about your appearance. You step on a scale and hear a voice of mockery about your weight. You buy a new outfit, and all you can hear is a revolting voice breaking you down about how you look. Brothers and sisters, these are *all lies*. Satan knows exactly what to whisper in our ears to make us think about ourselves in disgust. We have all fallen in his traps multiple times, but it's time that comes to a stop.

It's time to finally put those whispers and lies to an end. Don't let those lies run your life, but instead, look to the Father so that He can set you free. The next time you look in a mirror, step on a scale, put on a piece of clothing, I want you to tell yourself this, "I am perfectly made in Christ." I want you to say it and believe it. There's no amount of pounds, type of clothing, or looks that make you any less worthy of God's love. He loved you before you were even created. However, instead of feeling sorry for yourself waiting for God to use you, start taking the time to improve yourself. Put forward that effort that will make you even more usable for God.

Chapter 8

ACCOUNTABILITY = SUCCESS

*Brothers and sisters, if someone is caught in a sin, you who
live by the Spirit should restore that person gently. But watch
yourselves, or you also may be tempted. Carry each other's
burdens, and in this way you will fulfill the law of Christ. If
anyone thinks they are something when they are not, they de-
ceive themselves. Each one should test their own actions. Then
they can take pride in themselves alone, without comparing
themselves to someone else, for each one should carry their
own load.*

Galatians 6:1–9

We are charged to take care of our fellow brothers and sisters in
Christ. Here in Galatians, we see several ways in which we
should help each other: lovingly expose sin, carry one another's burdens, and be sure not to compare ourselves to other Christ-followers.
We see here that we are told to help carry each other's burdens. Pretty
powerful, isn't it? What does it mean to carry a burden for someone
else?

I have a story about one of the greatest people I have had the pleasure of getting close to. My friend Bekah came into my life unexpectedly. My husband and I had just gotten settled into our new station in Fort Walton Beach, Florida. We didn't know a lot of people or have any friends. We hadn't found a church to call home yet, and I was feeling discouraged to not have a "family" around us. I remember my husband telling me he had a friend from his shop who had just gotten married and that we should meet up with them. I was quite taken aback at the suggestion because my husband is introverted, and hanging out with people isn't usually high on his to-do list. So I figured these people must be pretty great if he wanted us to go out and hang with them.

We decided to go play disc golf for our double date. We all gathered around the first pad, and Erik introduced Joe and me to his newly wedded wife, Bekah. I remember my first impression of Bekah. She was shy and quiet but looked very sweet and personable. I was intrigued to get to know her. I did the next best thing after introductions; I forgot her name. I was so nervous about meeting new people that her name slipped right out of my head. Apparently, I wasn't the only one, however, because when I whispered to Joe to ask what her name was, he couldn't remember either. It wasn't because she wasn't impactful or unimportant to us; we were both really nervous and bad with names.

So the entire eighteen holes, all I could do was make small talk with Bekah because I felt so guilty for forgetting her name. I wasn't humble enough to just admit that I forgot her name, so I just rolled with it. It was an awkward, pretty silent eighteen-hole game, and after we parted ways, I felt so guilty for not trying harder to get to know her.

After some time had passed, we decided to try our disc golfing date again. This time, Erik said her name right away, so I glued her name into my memory. From then on, our friendship seemed to blossom almost overnight. We started hanging out and even began working at the same coffee shop together. Now, I can't imagine our lives without those dear friends. They have made such an impact on us and have also provided us a family away from family.

As time went by, a terrible tragedy struck Bekah's family; they lost her mother. It was so hard to watch Bekah go through that time as I felt there was nothing I could do to really help. She was such an inspiration as even though times were hard, she never lost her faith in the Lord. She stayed as positive as she could and always tried to have a smile on her face. The only time you could ever tell something was up was when she would allow me to see it and try to comfort her. I remember during that time that our friendship grew closer because Bekah allowed me to be a part of her pain, her burden. I gladly helped (in what little ways I could) to help support her and her burdens.

I know that God placed that circumstance in all our lives because there was a lesson to be learned and ways to grow. I could never associate with Bekah that I understand at all what she went through, but I'm so thankful she allowed me to be there with her to help carry the load. So many things I learned as God revealed in my heart as I watched a woman of God prevail through hardship and pain to become an even more prominent Christ-follower. Not only did He work in Bekah and her family's life through the circumstance, but He also worked in mine.

Stopping to help our brother or sister in Christ is so important in our walk with God. *"Beloved, if God so loved us, we ought also to love one another"* (1 John 4:11). We have been called to love, support, and even carry those around us. I'm not trying to give myself a pat on the back for being involved in Bekah's situation; rather, I'm honored she would allow me to be a part of her life during that time and help her in whatever way I could. I merely share this story to give you an example of how God can use us to be there for other people.

Benefits of Accountability

Working on health goals can be a very personal task, right? We know exactly what our innermost thoughts, desires, insecurities, and failures are. Adjusting our lifestyle tends to resurface a lot of personal areas. I think that's why the devil can get such a hard grasp on someone's lifestyle because it can be so personal, and it's so easy to lie in wait and prey on those insecurities.

What would your first thought be if I told you that you might need someone in your health journey to help push you over the hills and bumps along the way? Maybe you're already shaking your head no because you don't want to share what you're going through. Perhaps you've let someone in before, and they hurt you for it. I get it; I've been there. When you finally open up to someone about your health, it can be a scary road. But when your heart is in the right place to honor God, you might be surprised that this time is different. I encourage you to look for someone that has a godly heart and has the desire to lift up others. Maybe that person is way different than someone you would have generally asked.

Let me ask you this: If you're going down this road to start a God-centered healthy lifestyle, why would you ask someone who doesn't have the same values? They won't be able to encourage you in a biblical setting, only how they know to encourage in the world. Finding a Christ-follower will be able to help guide you and bring your attention back to God on the hard days. When everything seems to be going wrong, or life just happens, that godly friend can help you turn your attention and need back on God.

Maybe you struggle to think of a personal friend with those attributes. Instead of looking in your close circle, maybe look to your church family. Is there someone you connect with that is a godly influence on your life? They might be the perfect choice for you to fellowship, create a friendship, and have a godly accountability partner. God has given us resources for help if we are willing to look. "Oh, that's weird to reach out to my church family for health and fitness." Is it really? We are all a part of the body of Christ. The more effectively we can serve, the more we can do for the body. If you are able to improve yourself to serve more, why wouldn't a church member want to help you?

In this day and age, we've made health and fitness totally separate from the church. Our current way of life doesn't point to the importance of a healthy body as we do a healthy soul. Of course, to choose one over the other, the soul is much more important. But the body isn't something to ignore. I know that's why God has put this information on my heart to share. We need to be focusing on taking care of ourselves and helping others do the same. It's time to start improving the body of Christ spiritually, mentally, and even physically. The more we can do for Christ, the more we honor Him. Why don't you look for that person today and begin your journey to honor Christ?

Find One Who You Trust

You probably have guessed where I'm going with this. We need each other not only in our spiritual walks but in our physical walks as well. When you take the journey of improving your physical health, it's possible to do it on your own, but oh so hard. There are so many snares and tribulations you go through mentally and spiritually that it makes it so hard to stay encouraged on your own. For anyone wanting to start a new healthy lifestyle, it's so important to find that one friend, that one accountability partner that can be with you the whole way.

I encourage you to find someone you really trust. Someone in your life that you would share personal information with. The person you choose needs to be your confidant that you share your innermost reasons for wanting to change your lifestyle. They should know your goals, dreams, plan of action, temptations, progress, and hard days. A good partner can make the difference between a great health journey and a miserable one.

On days you don't feel motivated to be active, reach out to your partner. When you're tempted to strive towards worldly actions, unhealthy habits, share those situations. Let that confidant be there to help return you to godly thinking. Having someone to be accountable to (obviously, God is first on that priority) can help you succeed in healthy biblical living.

Maybe it's hard for you to reach out to someone for such a personal task; I get that. I would encourage you then to sit down in prayer and really ask for that person who can be a light for you. But know this, maybe God won't send you a dear friend. Maybe that person is your spouse. It can be hard opening up about those personal thoughts and desires, but it has the ability to grow you even closer. I'll admit sometimes it's really difficult to explain to my husband that I'm struggling to love how God has made my body. But I'll say this; there's nothing more encouraging to me personally than my husband telling me he loves exactly how I'm made. Not only does it renew my confidence, but it also reminds me to love what God has made and not what the world wants me to think. Perhaps that confidant is your children. Scary thought, right? Children have the wonderful talent of being completely and utterly honest. Sometimes too honest. But maybe a little bit of honest opinion is what you need. Maybe your children's thoughts and opinions are what you need to motivate you even more. Do your children want a healthy momma that can go outside and play with them? Do they want a dad that can take them out on adventures and not struggle to keep up? How much motivation could you ask for?

I believe God has put someone or maybe several someones in your life to help you through this time. It probably won't be in a way you expect, but it'll be what you need. Take time today to pray for that honest person, that godly encouragement that can help you succeed.

Be the Confidant

On the flip side of things, I would bet you know someone who is wanting to improve their health. Perhaps it is a coworker, a friend, family member, or spouse. Most of us in our lives know more than one person who wants to become healthier. As we have been discovering in this chapter about letting someone be there for us to lift us up, it's now time to focus on others to lift them up.

Just as we want to find that godly encouragement that can help us in our fitness journey, we need to be that stronghold for them as well. That should be an easy task, right? Actually, it's a little more challenging than you think. You have to *be there* for that person mentally, physically, and especially spiritually. You are that individual who needs to encourage them on days when everything goes wrong, to keep their heads up when they don't feel like they've made much progress. You also need to be that person who can call them out in areas that they are struggling with.

I want to share a story about a person who has impacted my life with his story. It's a brutal, blood, sweat, and tears kind of life, but it has convicted my heart more times than I can count. There was actually a movie based on this man's life, *Hacksaw Ridge*. The story the movie tells is about a man so convicted about not carrying a gun into war, for which he is endlessly ridiculed. He feels a call to serve as a medic but doesn't feel right about taking a life. What a conviction and an example of a man wanting to serve his heavenly Father.

In the movie, which is based on his real life, Desmond Doss grows up learning hard lessons about loving others, serving others, and being a faithful man of God. He finally feels a call to join the army to help aid men during World War II. His family and soon-to-be bride are nervous for him and what lies ahead, as he refuses to carry a gun. During basic training, he is kicked down more times than we can count by fellow soldiers, men in charge, and even the closest people in his life. He is ostracized by his fellow soldiers for being a pacifist, but Doss stands his ground. One particular soldier makes it his personal goal to take Doss out. Through beatings and belittling, Doss never throws a punch back. He is eventually threatened with a court-martial, but God takes the situation in His hands, and Doss is able to graduate. When he is actually at Hacksaw Ridge—the place was nicknamed due to its bloody history—Desmond Doss jumps right into action by saving any falling man he can. All the while never carrying a gun and never killing a soul. Towards the end of the movie, the platoon has to retreat on the hill because it is getting taken over. They order an air raid to help, and all the men clear out. All but one. During the raid, into nightfall, Doss sneaks around, finding wounded men and lowering them down by a rope to others for help.

At this point in the movie, your heart is racing as you watch this man single-handedly find multiple wounded, carry them to the edge of the fifty-foot ride, and then lift them down to safety. Doss finally falls down in exhaustion, hands bleeding, and almost defeated. Doss asks a single question, "Lord, help me get one more." Other soldiers that disagreed with his convictions ended up being saved by him. People's attitudes start to change, as they no longer see what they thought was a coward but the bravest man alive.

The man in basic training that tried to make Doss's life miserable ends up saving his life and becoming his friend. The man loses his life, and Doss fights to save him but is too late. Even at the end, when the Japanese are trying to kill Doss, he lowers himself and his deceased friend down the cliff. Towards the end of the movie, the same group is charged to retake Hacksaw again, but they won't do it unless Doss is with them. They all ask for Doss to pray before they begin because they are starting to believe in what Doss believes.

Doss eventually is wounded and lowered down the ridge by his comrades. Countless awards and honors were given to Desmond Doss for his outstanding courage during battle. Through all his medals, he still remained a humble man.

This story makes me wish I had an ounce of the courage, strength, and love that Doss had. Even though all of the soldiers made Doss's life miserable, Doss always treated them all with love, and with God's strength, he even saved their lives. If that's not a definition of a godly friend, then I don't know what is.

I'm not saying you need to be the next Desmond Doss, but I do think there are many things we can learn from his story. We need to be prepared to be hated in this world for our convictions but to stand up for what we believe in. We need to love those around us even if they don't love us back. Finally, we need to be that soldier for others, willing to help them in whatever situation, even if it's hard. And it will get hard, but that's when you stop and ask God, "Please, help me get one more." He will give you the strength you need to be that light for someone else.

When that friend comes to you needing help with their journey, be that help and more. Lift them up during hard times. Challenge them in their convictions when this world wants them to cave in. Don't let the enemy win even the smallest battle. Even if that battle is staying true to God and honoring Him with your bodies. God can use you as a soldier in whatever battle may come, and you should be ready to fight side by side with those around you. Won't you today be that helping hand, that loving and trusting friend they can depend on?

SECTION 2:

FITNESS AND NUTRITION FACTS

In this section of the book, we are going to shift gears from the previous chapters. Part one of the book teaches you the importance of putting God in your healthy living lifestyle. All of the tools in the previous chapters must be applied before you jump to section two. Let me remind you of this, if you try to skip the first section and just hop to the information in the second, you will ultimately fail. You may have progress and results, but your heart and body will not be serving our heavenly Father. Your time spent to change your life will be a waste because you are not doing it for the right reasons. So please, don't skip the first section. Take it to heart and apply it.

I'm so excited for you to jump into the second section of the book. This section is where we will get down to the nitty-gritty, the scientific and factual. The true facts proven scientifically of how to take care of your body. But don't worry, this section won't go into all of those big, fancy words and topics you have to read two times through to understand. I don't believe that this information should be hard or confusing. Rather, I want this information to be so easy, so accessible that anyone is able to try and apply the tools to their life.

We will also talk about debunking current fitness, health, and nutrition fads. A skill not commonly taught in today's world. You may not see it now, but there are hundreds of fads that are just scams, money-makers, poorly taught, and have little scientific evidence to back up their programs. I think this is a hugely important area to teach others so that no matter what new device Dr. Oz decides to promote on his next show, you will be able to break it down to decide whether it is worth your time and money. So without further ado, let's take this journey to the next level so you can learn how to truly better your body.

Chapter 9

BEHAVIOR CHANGE IS A MUST

We've talked about how we need to have the right heart for God before we even start focusing on a health and fitness program. The same is true when you apply actual habits to your physical lifestyle. Motivators. What our true motivators are is our strongest connection for staying dedicated to any type of program. We cannot expect ourselves to be dedicated to a program if our intentions are weak. Weak intentions lead to two things: a fast burnout and a dislike for any health program. As a personal trainer and health coach, the worst thing I can see happen to a client is to have an experience that makes them dislike health and fitness even more.

It's kind of like when you were in physical education in school or in a sport. If someone was acting up, the teacher or coach usually dished out a physical challenge as a punishment. Now don't get me wrong, I loved my PE teachers and coaches. I think there is a lot of value in being challenged to push past your mental capacity in physical fitness to see what you're really capable of.

For example, in my junior year of high school, I was the lead libero for my volleyball team. We had Regionals approaching us, and practice was a critical and crucial time. Everything from simple passing, setting, serving, and hitting was drilled over and over again. Game situations and certain plays were drilled into our heads so that we were as capable and confident as we could be. There were certain drills, however, that our team would struggle with. Sometimes it was due to lack of trying; other times, we struggled to communicate or even work together as a team. Let me tell you, that never sat well with Coach Patrone.

Coach Patrone was one of the most influential coaches in my life. She wasn't afraid to put her foot down, to be the hard coach. But she also had a wonderful, caring side that valued each and every one of her players. On the court, when drills would go wrong or balls dropped on the floor, all the players would stop and cringe, waiting for the punishment. Coach was never one to let laziness rule the court. I can't count how many times we ran, did sprints, hard exercise challenges that would make our legs burn until we could barely walk. She was known for pushing her players, but she was also known for producing great players.

Back to Regionals. My team was trying to perform a very specific, controlled passing and setting drill. The drill required a lot of movement, tons of communication, and unrelenting focus. Little to say, our team had little of anything that day and struggled to finish the drill. After a couple of failed attempts, Coach finally was annoyed with us and decided for us to "get on the line." Literally one of the worst phrases that still makes my stomach turn today. We would sprint what was called a five in thirty. For this exercise, we had to run the length of the volleyball court up and back, which was one, five times in under thirty seconds. For the first one you do, it's very easy; you can usually finish your five sprints in twenty to twenty-five if you work hard. However, the more you run, the harder it gets, and if one person doesn't cross the line in thirty seconds, the drill doesn't count. So this was the punishment of choice usually when we weren't getting things done. Well, we ran our five in thirty and tried our drill again. We failed, back to the line. Drill, then more running, another drill, and again more running. I've never had my legs feel so numb with exhaustion. Finally, thirty minutes over our normal practice time, drill still uncompleted, Coach decided to call it a day. However, she wanted to return to our drill the next day. I'm pretty sure all of us just lay on the floor trying to remember how to breathe for a solid five minutes. As we lay there, we contemplated how many sprints we actually ran that day. We estimated we had run somewhere between 120–130 sprints total. No wonder my legs were numb. I will tell you this, even though that was one of the hardest practices I ever had, I learned so much about how far I could go. I've never forgotten that experience and never will.

I don't tell you this story to make you cringe thinking of how bad exercise can be. I tell you this story because it's important to know the difference between the right kind of "push" and the wrong kind of "push." I believe my coach had every right in the world to make us run as much as we did because we weren't improving, and we needed an ultimatum. But our team also had a really big goal for all that sweat and tears; we were going to make it to state. But if we hadn't had a good goal, if we were just running to get in shape, then we would have walked away hating the very thought of exercise. It would have ruined our motivation to even think about running or sprinting again. What a horrible thought to think someone out there has had that detrimental experience that has ruined their desire to be active. Mind you, some of you might have had a bad experience in sports or PE that turned you away from fitness. The same idea applies to some of you, as you may have subjected yourself to a ridiculously hard workout program that immediately put a bad taste in your mouth for activity.

I am sorry if you ever had a bad experience with exercise; I know how that goes. However, I want to encourage you that what I will teach you won't be the expectation to run 120–130 sprints to get in good shape. I'm not going to tell you to up and join a Crossfit gym to see results. You may want to do those things, which are fine, but with the right mindset to use your body for the activity you feel God could use you for, it can be much simpler. It all starts with a little behavior change and intervention.

Intervention for Every Unique Individual

"No temptation has overtaken you that is not common to man. God is faithful, and he will not let you be tempted beyond your ability, but with the temptation he will also provide the way of escape, that you may be able to endure it" (1 Corinthians 10:13).

The first step with intervention is to find out your "hows" and "whys" that you want to change. Know that no matter what your situation is, God will never give you a circumstance you can't do. He is with you always, and as my favorite verse quotes, *"I can do all things through Christ who strengtheneth me"* (Philippians 4:13). He

138

will give you the strength that you need to change.

The change you desire to pursue starts with internal or external factors. Internal factors are motivated by: knowledge of risks, benefits of risk reduction, personal beliefs and core values, self-efficacy, and social and adaption skills. When you want to change your health because you want to be active with your grandchildren, that is an internal motivator. When you're a mother of three and you want a better lifestyle to provide for your children, that is an internal motivator. What is an external motivator? External is when you are motivated by social support, socio-culture, economic and political factors, health care system, environmental stressors, and societal laws and regulations. So, needless to say, external motivators come from a feeling of requirement. Your doctor tells you your health needs to improve. Your golfing buddies are concerned for your health and tell you to take care of yourself. Your environment at work is stressful but would be manageable if your health was in better shape. All of those examples are types of external motivators.

Now both motivators are good reasons to start exercising; however, studies show that internal motivators are the most effective and consistent to encourage someone to continue chasing after a better lifestyle. When you have a desire to improve your health that's personal, you have a goal you don't want to let down. You think of the people you want to lift up and stay true to.

A friend of mine recently decided she wanted to improve her health. At first, she told me she wanted to lose weight, but after some honest conversations, we really dug to find the real reason for exer-

139

cise. My friend wanted to improve her health so that she would be able to live a longer, healthier life for her family. She didn't want a poor lifestyle to be the cause of leaving her family earlier than she was supposed to. Talk about an internal motivator! She wanted to be healthy so she could help take care of her grandbabies and the family.

When times get hard, when life hits and you sit there wondering, *Why am I putting in the effort to do this?* I will bet you you will be much more dedicated to continuing when you think of your family, kids, spouse rather than the reason of your golf buddies telling you to. In those moments, we tell ourselves that our golf buddies don't understand because they're not the ones that have to do the work. Sounds a little harsh, maybe. But am I right? Internal motivators will be the difference between you starting a program and sticking with it. While all motivators are important to address, only one will truly be the reason for your behavior change.

Transtheoretical Model and How to Apply It

I'm going to get a little "sciency" with you now. We're going to talk about the importance of the Transtheoretical Model. I know, it's a big word. I must say that I feel quite profound being able to use it in a sentence. But I don't throw this new vocabulary word at you just to make myself look smart. Trust me; I'm no Albert Einstein. Thankfully, however, someone dumbed down the inner workings of the body easily enough that even I can understand and teach it. If I can do that, then you got this.

The Transtheoretical Model (TTM) *"states that individuals' be-*

140

haviors are based on their readiness or stage of change" (Battista 2018). Basically, what we've been talking about since the beginning is that you need to have a good state of mind and heart to be ready to change your lifestyle. Those very smart people in the American College of Sports Medicine found that the TTM is based on five different levels of readiness. Now, as a quick note, there are several theories that identify different factors for people, and as personal trainers, we are to find the one that fits the best for the client. Out of all the six theories that I could bore you with (even though they are all good theories nonetheless), I personally find the TTM is the simplest and one of the more effective to recommend to clients. Now that being said, here are the five stages that I want you to pay attention to:

1. Precontemplation: an individual is not ready to take action and is not considering the benefits of a healthier lifestyle at this point.

2. Contemplation: now, an individual is considering the negative consequences of their current lifestyle and is now considering changing within the next six months.

3. Preparation: the individual now has a plan to start behavior change and will be doing so within the next thirty days.

4. Action: the individual is now currently making behavior changes in their lifestyle and has been for less than six months.

5. Maintenance: our individual now is continuing the maintenance of their new active lifestyle (more than six months) and is making it a goal to not relapse.

So what does all of this TTM stuff mean? Basically, the importance of realizing this model is to prepare yourself for change properly. We have now identified different points of life that people are in when they are thinking of changing their lifestyle. However, many people tend to jump from stage one to stage four without preparing. Those people tend to end up burning out.

Example time. How many people do you know (maybe even including yourself) have suddenly made a New Year's resolution to lose weight? I can't even begin to count for you! I've been there, done that. Many people do! At first, their journey of realization is that their need to change motivates them so much that they go out and buy memberships, programs, food programs, clothing, and the like. We drop all of our money on this idea that we are more motivated now than ever before, and this time it's going to work. It works for about thirty days, maybe sixty. We go so hard and so fast in the gym, working out at home, sweating our little behinds off. We feel good about the fact that we're working hard, getting closer to our goal. Suddenly, life happens. Family situations pop up. Friends are in dire need. Work gets stressful, and days are stretched. Suddenly, that diet you've been forcing yourself to stick to doesn't seem too important anymore. You're exhausted, tired, and just want a break. Well, you take your break for a couple of days. Days turn to weeks; weeks turn into months; months turn into a year. One day, we wake up and realize we are right back where we were or even worse off than when we started. The next New Year hits, and somehow, we foolishly convince ourselves to do it all over again! This is a common, ugly cycle people get stuck in all the time.

Remember a couple of chapters before we talked about the importance of really taking our time? That's basically what the TTM is trying to teach you. A healthier lifestyle is just around the corner for you, but you can't expect yourself to get there by just jumping in and hoping it works. Like many things in life, when it comes to actual adulting, we have to sit down and plan this healthier lifestyle out. And unlike many things in today's world, you have to realize it will take effort, dedication, and a lot of time. No more sixty-day instant fix stuff.

With the TTM in mind, I now want you to take some time and figure out which stage you are currently in. Do you know you have certain health issues that you talk about wanting to improve? Maybe you're sitting at the Contemplation stage, and you didn't even know it. Have you decided it's time to change, and that's why you started reading this book? It might be that you're at the Preparation stage. Whatever stage you are in, first and foremost, be honest with yourself. Don't skip ahead because that will only cause the "new year, new me" fantasy again. Instead, do the hard thing and take the time to find out where you are.

Behavior Change Is Worth It—Now Apply It

So we've talked about internal vs. external motivators. We broke down the TTM and learned how it could apply to each of our unique stages. Now is the time, are you ready? To finally apply all of those tools and implement lasting behavioral changes.

When it comes to actual behavioral changes, those need to happen in the later stages of change to work effectively.

143

Examples of cognitive processes of change, which are effectively used in the precontemplation, contemplation, and preparation stages include increasing awareness about the problems related to sedentary behavior (consciousness raising), assessing how being active or inactive affects a person's life (environmental reevaluation), evaluating oneself as an active person or couch potato (self-reevaluation), or helping clients identify moments of emotion related to physical activity (dramatic relief). Examples of behavioral processes of change... include removing cues for sedentary behavior (stimulus control), action and maintenance stages, including removing cues for sedentary behavior (stimulus control), finding support for active behaviors (helping relationships), and reinforcing positive behaviors (reinforcement management).

Battista 2018, 204

Basically, when you swap out your bad habits for good habits, you are now implementing good behavior change. When you consistently and habitually apply these newfound habits, that's when you really start to notice change in your everyday lifestyle. With good habits, you can start to feel better, look better, lose weight, and adapt to a totally new lifestyle that can last you for the rest of your life.

When I say that it's worth it to be able to implement good behaviors, I mean it. A lot of people think there's some magic trick to losing weight or becoming healthier, but honestly, it all starts with adopting good habits and sticking to them. Even though many people may try to adopt good habits, most do it in an unrealistic way, so they don't stick. However, if you follow through with the TTM of change find your internal and external motivators, I think you'll find it is a lot easier to pursue better habits.

Just as we talked about in the first couple chapters about having the right heart for God, you need to have the right motivators to encourage your heart to put in the work. So I want you to take a couple of minutes and really think about what your external and internal motivators are. Also, remember, whatever your motivators are, make sure they will be goals that will honor and glorify God. Find three external and three internal motivators in your life. Once you've done that, narrow your motivators down to one each and decide if they first honor God, secondly, give you the motivation and confidence to start a new lifestyle, and thirdly, will be your make it or break it reasons.

Chapter 10

BEHAVIOR CHANGE IS A MUST

Whoever dwells in the shelter of the Most High will rest in the shadow of the Almighty. I will say of the Lord, "He is my refuge and my fortress, my God, in whom I trust." Surely he will save you from the fowler's snare and from the deadly pestilence. He will cover you with his feathers, and under his wings you will find refuge; his faithfulness will be your shield and rampart. You will not fear the terror of the night, nor the arrow that flies by day, nor the pestilence that stalks in the darkness, nor the plague that destroys at midday...If you say, "The Lord is my refuge," and you make the Most High your dwelling, no harm will overtake you, no disaster will come near your tent. For he will command his angels concerning you to guard you in all your ways; they will lift you up in their hands, so that you will not strike your foot against a stone. "Because he loves me," says the Lord, "I will rescue him; I will protect him, for he acknowledges my name."

Psalm 91:1–6, 9–12, 14

Sometimes I think people shy away from starting down a healthier road because they're worried about the unknown. There are so many "what ifs" that people can think of that it makes them think that it's not worth it in the long run. *What if I'm not strong enough? I have bad knees; I could never try to be active again. What if I hurt myself and end up worse than before? Working out is hard, and I don't think I have it in me to do it.* All of these thoughts and more are valid concerns that people can have about changing their lifestyle. I mean, who can blame us? We all get comfortable in a way that we go about life, and to change it seems almost impossible or improbable. Here's the thing, changing your life will never be easy. I heard a really great quote from a friend of mine the other day.

> *Marriage is hard, divorce is hard—choose your hard. Being overweight and out-of-shape is hard. Staying fit and trim is hard. Choose your hard. Being in debt is hard. Being financially responsible is hard. Choose your hard. Having broken and unhealthy relationships is hard. Maintaining healthy relationships with friends and family is hard. Choose your hard.*
>
> —Steve Campbell

Many of those hard situations listed in that quote are truly difficult no matter which way you turn. However, at some point, we decide that one of them is worth more than the other. Taking a road to rebuilding your marriage instead of letting it fall into divorce would be so hard, but not impossible. It would be impossible on your own, but if you were to put your faith in God for that situation, then He will never let you down. The same applies to choosing to start a healthier lifestyle. It will be hard. It will challenge you. You will want to give back in to your "easy," "regular" desires of your old self. "*...but with God all things are possible*" (Matthew 19:26). That's the ticket! "But God!" There are no ifs or hows or whys, only "but God." You don't need to know anything else except that He will be the one to get you through this, no matter how impossible it may seem.

I shared with you the scripture from Psalm 91. The supposed author of Psalm 91 was thought to be Moses during his forty years wandering in the wilderness. He wrote the literal dangers they came across in their time, fowler, plague, pestilence, terror, animals, etc. Even though we may not have those exact same issues today, there is an underlying message here for Christians in today's world. In reference to the forty years, Paul tells us, "...these things were to our examples..." (1 Corinthians 10:6) So in Psalm 91, we are shown an example of how to put our trust in God and the many ways He will protect us from all that is around us.

Are you going to trust God today with this new direction He's put on your heart? Or will you struggle to put your faith in Him? A new, healthy, godly-lived physical life can only start one way, and that's when God is in the center. So I encourage you today to stop making those same excuses you've made for every other program that's come your way. Stop repeating the same mistakes and failures from the past when things have gotten too hard. Instead, it's time to put your trust in God and let Him lead you each step of the way.

149

Health Screening Is a Must

Now that we are actually to the very exciting point of applying all of the biblical lessons into the fitness world, it is so important to make sure you are ready to start a health and fitness program. I don't say this to discourage you in thinking this will take time away from your program, but I do say this to keep you safe. As a personal trainer myself, I have to always inform all of my clients that they must go through a few simple health screening evaluations so that we can find if there are any underlying health risks.

It may sound kind of funny to actually start getting into the small, little details like health screening at this point, but I'm dead serious. I would not be a good trainer, a good friend, or a good sister-in-Christ if I didn't encourage you to go the correct route. For your safety and the longevity of a program, it is absolutely necessary for you to start with health screening. Here's a fun fact, those who hate having to take the time to go through the screening process will more than likely hurt themselves either minorly or seriously, which in the long run takes much longer for them to be able to get on track with their health. However, if you can somehow find your patience, trust me and do this right. It will pay off.

At the end of this chapter, I will have some links for you to follow to find a couple of forms that will allow you to screen yourself for any health risks. There are basically two approaches that the American College of Sports Medicine (ACSM) asks that you follow. You can either self-screen yourself without the input of an exercise professional or hire one to do it for you. There is no wrong answer here. If you don't feel comfortable doing it yourself, then I would suggest asking your doctor to help you get a health screening or to suggest someone who can do it for you. The form included at the end of this chapter is a self-guided one that will easily point you in the right direction you need to go. The PAR-Q+ is a physical activity readiness questionnaire for everyone. Taking this questionnaire will be easy, take less than ten minutes, and it will inform you if you need to seek further advice from your doctor or a qualified exercise professional before becoming physically active.

I want to make this perfectly clear, if you take the PAR-Q+ and find that you need to delay exercise to get a physician's go-ahead first, *do not skip this!* There are reasons the big wigs up top have made these requirements, and they are to keep you safe. Trust me; you will be so much happier, healthier, and safer to go the right route instead of going it alone on your own. I mean, reading this book will be very pointless if you basically ignore what it has to say, so maybe try to listen. When you take your questionnaire, it's basically going to be searching for these main things:

» Are you currently physically active?

» Do you have any cardiovascular, metabolic, and/or renal diseases (CMR)?

» Do you or do you not have signs and/or symptoms of any of those diseases?

Now those questions may not make a lot of sense to you, and that's okay. They're basically fishing out those of you who could have potential risks if you were to start too much physical activity too vigorously. This is not to point you out or make you feel worse about your condition. Actually, if you fall under those categories, then it's even more vital for you to improve your health. But when there are people that have certain flags that come up, then there is a certain order of events that must be taken.

You will learn some of this in the PAR-Q+, but I want to make this very easy for everyone. There are basically eight different categories you can fall into:

» If you are not currently exercising and have no cardiovascular, metabolic, and/or renal disease (CMR) with no signs or symptoms, you will be given the go-ahead to start a program with light to moderate physical activity.

» If you are not currently exercising, have no CMR diseases, but have signs and/or symptoms of those diseases, then you *must* get medical clearance from your physician before you can start exercising. Only then will you be able to start at a light or moderate physical activity level.

» If you are not currently exercising and have a CMR disease but no signs and/or symptoms, you still *must* get a physician's clearance before you start exercising. Once you have clearance, you can start at a light to moderate physical activity level.

» If you are not currently exercising and have a CMR disease and signs and/or symptoms, it is *vital* that you get a medical clearance from your physician before exercising. Once approved, only then can you start a light to moderate exercise program.

» If you are currently exercising, have no CMR disease, and have no signs and/or symptoms, you can start physical activity at a moderate or vigorous level of intensity.

» If you are currently exercising, have no CMR disease but do have signs and/or symptoms, you need to *immediately stop* exercising and get medical clearance from your physician before starting a program.

» If you are currently exercising and have a CMR disease but no signs and/or symptoms, you can start at a moderate intensity for physical activity but must have medical clearance from your physician if you want to go to vigorous intensity.

» If you are currently exercising and have a CMR disease and signs and/or symptoms, you need to *immediately stop* exercising and get medical clearance from your physician before continuing to exercise.

So what are the different kinds of signs and/or symptoms that you should make yourself aware of? Great question. Again, this information will also be in the questionnaire you take at the end, but I want to make this very simplified for everyone so it's easy to understand on your own. These are signs and/or symptoms you should assess if you have:

- » chest discomfort with exertion
- » unreasonable breathlessness
- » dizziness, fainting, blackouts
- » ankle swelling
- » unpleasant awareness of a forceful, rapid, or irregular heart rate
- » burning or cramping sensations in your lower legs when walking short distances
- » heart murmurs

Do any of those sound familiar, or have you been diagnosed with any of those symptoms? Again, if you experience any of those signs or symptoms, then you must stop exercising if you are currently, or before you start exercising, you need to get cleared by a medical professional first. All of the signs and symptoms have been pointed out for a reason, as they normally can be linked back to a more serious health issue. If that health issue is not addressed properly, then exercising can make the condition worse if it is not handled correctly.

Now there are some contraindications to exercise that you also need to be aware of. Certain things that may have happened in your health can have an effect on the safety of pursuing any exercise at all. It is an absolute contradiction if you have ever had:

- » acute myocardial infarction in the past two days
- » ongoing unstable angina
- » uncontrolled cardiac arrhythmia with hemodynamic compromise
- » active endocarditis
- » symptomatic severe aortic stenosis
- » decompensated heart failure
- » acute pulmonary embolism, pulmonary infarction, or deep venous thrombosis
- » acute myocarditis or pericarditis
- » acute aortic dissection
- » physical disability that precludes safe and adequate testing

If any of those conditions ring a bell to you, or you know for absolute certainty that you have experienced one or more of those, then you need to again consult with your doctor about what the best plan of action can be for you at this time. Now there are also a couple of relative contraindications that you may want to be aware of as well:

- » known obstructive left main coronary artery stenosis
- » moderate to severe aortic stenosis with an uncertain relationship to symptoms
- » tachyarrhythmias with uncontrolled ventricular rates
- » acquired advanced or complete heart block

» recent stroke or transient ischemic attack

» mental impairment with limited ability to cooperate

» resting hypertension with systolic >200 mmHg or diastolic >110 mmHg

» uncorrected medical conditions, such as significant anemia, important electrolyte imbalance, and hyperthyroidism

So now that all of that super fun medical stuff is out of the way, we can continue on practicing safe and healthy habits that will promote your future, yay!

What Are Your Risk Factors?

I know I said we were done with the super fun medical stuff, which we are, but now we jump into a whole new deal entirely. This section is specifically talking about risk factors. Now risk factors used to be the mandatory component for deciding if you could exercise with or without medical clearance, but that's changed with our new questionnaire that has come out. However, risk factors are still important as they help as a tool for identifying and controlling cardiovascular disease risk management and prevention. So I would encourage all of you, young or old, to take a minute to scan through these different areas of risks that could point out some important areas you didn't know you had a connection to. The way this works is determined by the amount of risk factors you have, which are considered positive. If you have one or none, then you have a very low risk of future cardiovascular disease. If you have two or more risk factors, then you have an increased risk for disease. As a fun side note, out of all the risk factors, I will show you there is one negative risk factor (having high high-density lipoprotein [HDL-C]). Basically, a high HDL helps reverse cholesterol transport and can help lower the risk of cardiovascular disease. If you have a negative risk factor, it actually offsets a positive risk factor. So if you had two positives and then a high HDL, you would only have one positive risk factor remaining. Cool, huh? So let's dive into the risk factors. Do you have any of the following?

» Client's age of forty-five years or older for males and fifty-five years or older for females.

» Family history of specific cardiovascular events: heart attack, bypass surgery or angioplasty, or sudden cardiac death. Only apply this to first-degree relatives, so your biological parents, siblings, and children. The risk factor applies if any of those relatives had one of the three events before hitting the age of fifty-five for men or sixty-five for females.

» You currently smoke cigarettes, have quit in the last six months, or have been exposed to secondhand smoke regularly.

» Currently inactive by not participating in a regular exercise program or not meeting the minimal recommendations for exercise of doing thirty minutes or more of moderate physical activity at least three days a week for three months.

» Obesity. This is defined as a Body Mass Index (BMI) of thirty or a waist circumference of 102 cm, which is about forty inches for men and greater than 88 cm or also as thirty-five inches for women.

» Hypertension. If your resting blood pressure is equal to or above 140 mmHg systolic and also if your diastolic is equal to or above 90 mmHg. Also, if you are taking any antihypertensive medications.

» You struggle with dyslipidemia, which is having a low-density lipoprotein cholesterol (LDL-C) that is equal to or above 130 mg and also an HDL-C of less than 40 mg, or you are taking a lipid-lowering medication that is also a positive risk factor.

» You have diabetes and have a fasting plasma glucose of equal to or greater than 126 mg (7.0 mmol) or two-hour plasma glucose values in an oral glucose tolerance test of equal or greater than 200 mg or an HbA1C that's greater or equal to 6.5 percent.

» Lastly, do you have a high-serum HDL-C that is equal to or greater than 60 mg? This is the negative risk factor that can offset one positive risk factor.

All in all, there are a lot of risks that we need to be aware of that can affect our productivity and health to start exercising. Here's the thing that I want to encourage those of you with if you had to check a couple of these boxes: starting a healthier lifestyle is even more important for you. Yes, we all need to pursue a better lifestyle that can honor God with all that we do. But if you have one to several different medical situations that are present, then it is even more important for you to change the things you can by adapting your life to better living. You may not be able to start as soon or as vigorously as you wanted, but I promise you this, the smallest steps can equal the largest change. You may have diabetes, high blood pressure, risk for a heart attack or stroke. Can I say again that improving your lifestyle will help you in the long run? I didn't write this book just to help semi-healthy people get healthier. I wrote this book so that it can help *everyone and anyone*. My goal for all of you is to realize that whatever situation you have in this life, God will give you the help and the strength you need to use His body for His purpose.

Do you know how Christ compares the church as His bride? He makes the comparison to show that intimate connection that only man and wife would have, just as He wants for Him and His church. The same, I believe so deeply in my heart, applies to the Holy Spirit living inside our bodies. He wants that intimate connection to our hearts. The more that we take steps of faith so He can use us for His kingdom, the more intimate we become. So what am I saying? I'm saying that if you have the Holy Spirit living inside you, then it's time to become more intimate with your Maker by making His vessel more ready for His use. So please, don't let these risk assessments or questionnaires make you give up. This is only the beginning! Starting the right way will give you great success in the end. I always say that small habits equal great success. Starting with these small habits of change in your mind and body will be huge for you in the future. So stick with me; you're going to do great things as long as you trust in the Lord to get you through it so He can use your body.

Fitness Assessment

As promised, I have included a couple of different questionnaires for you to take. These are more general and probably a little easier to understand when trying to find out where you are starting. So take five to ten minutes and fill these out. These are self-lead, so be as honest as you can, and they'll point you in the direction you need to go.

» PAR-Q+: http://eparmedx.com/wp-content/uploads/2021/01/ParQ-Plus-Jan-2021-Image.pdf.

» Insert ePARmed-X+Online: http://eparmedx.com/?page_id =24.

Chapter 11

FACTS OF CARDIORESPIRATORY PROGRAMS

Therefore, since we are surrounded by such a great cloud of witnesses, let us throw off everything that hinders and the sin that so easily entangles. And let us run with perseverance the race marked out for us, fixing our eyes on Jesus, the pioneer and perfecter of faith. For the joy set before him he endured the cross, scorning its shame, and sat down at the right hand of the throne of God. Consider him who endured such opposition from sinners, so that you will not grow weary and lose heart.

Hebrews 12:1–3

If you read Hebrews chapter 11, you will read many, many examples of what true faith looks like. Faith that involves trusting God through different challenges. Faith that means to trust in God's promise for eternity and not only while living on earth. Then, when you jump into chapter 12, you will see many similar details applied from chapter 11. As we read about many heroic examples of faith and persecution, none being more of a greater example than Jesus's suffering and death, who showed faith unto God, His Father, through all of His hardships. Jesus believed that even though He was going through horrible circumstances, God had a plan behind it all, which He did. The same idea is applied to us that no matter whether we suffer little or a lot, we are to trust God has a plan. That our suffering for God is worth it all in the end, that we have to stay strong and finish our race.

We need to finish the race that God has set before us. What is that "race" that we have to run? Do we actually have to run it? Here's the answer; we need to go at whatever pace, and for how long, and do whatever it is that He laid out for us. Most likely, most of us won't know what our "race" looks like until we've run it. We won't know how hard it may be, how long it may go, or what obstacles it will hold. What we do know is that God is with us every step of the race and has asked us to place our faith in Him during it. I have to wonder if God has explained our faith being tested like us running a race; surely, He knew that we needed endurance and strength to get us through to the end.

Now, remember we can train as hard as we possibly can, and it will never amount to the true strength and endurance God can grant us with His power. However, I believe that He's also telling us to use our bodies to go out there and conquer what He's laid out for us. Let me ask you this way, right now, where you're sitting, could you go out there and run that race He laid out for you? Could you physically perform in the ways you need to, or would you say no to race because of your health? Don't you want to be prepared to run that race for whatever calling you may get? Do you want to be restricted by poor health you could have prevented, or do you want to better yourself so that you can be put to the test? I know I do, and I want to be ready no matter where I am at in life.

God designed us with legs, lungs, muscles for endurance, oxygen to be absorbed, food to be used as energy, and many other million small moving parts that work together to make us run. It wasn't by accident He enabled us to be running creatures; He planned that! He knew we would need the ability to outrun danger, to pursue a prize, and yes, to finish a race.

So am I going to tell you to go out there and start running? No, that would be ridiculous and naive of me. Not all of us can run, not all of us have the desire to run, and certainly, not all of us want to do it all the time. But what I do want to tell you is that cardiorespiratory fitness is vital for our overall health to be able to go out there and run. Now mind you, your "race" may not involve literal running. Your race may be walking slowly to the finish line. Your race may be a hard crawl. We all will have a different race to perform, but we need to strengthen the one thing that enables us to perform for our race, cardiorespiratory fitness.

Don't roll your eyes; please stick with me here. I know there are trainers out there that say you don't have to do cardio to get in shape. There are those nutrition gurus that say you don't even have to exercise to lose weight. Remember my goal here is not to just get you to lose those pounds. My goal is to teach you the proven ways you can get fit and healthy and how you can maintain it to be the best servant you can be for our heavenly Father. Do you see the difference? I'm telling you that participating in cardio exercise will be beneficial for

163

your lifelong health, and it will prepare you to be an active "runner" for God for whatever may come your way. Yes, I know you can't prepare for everything, especially when God decides to throw some refining fire your way, but you can be prepared to be the best you can be. You can take care of what you've been given to bring honor and glory to God. That's what I'm trying to tell you.

Is Cardio the Magic Weight Loss Key?

In all the social media today that talks about the surefire exercise programs that will cause you to lose weight, do they actually work, and is it the key to getting in the best shape? Here's my answer that I've found from a recent study done by the American College of Sports Medicine, *"The scientific evidence demonstrating the beneficial effects of exercise is indisputable, and the benefits of exercise far outweigh the risks in most adults."* The results are showing that cardio, resistance training, flexibility, and neuromotor training are essential for adults. So yes, exercise can help us lose weight and get healthier, but cardio is not just the key component. Like we've talked about before, exercise and nutrition go hand-in-hand to make the perfect balance of overall good health. So cardiorespiratory training is a part of the necessary combination to make everything work well. You can go straight ahead with your P90X workouts, your boot camp workouts, the elliptical, running, High Intensity Interval Training (HIIT). All of those can make you work and will improve your cardio health, but it shouldn't be the only aspect of your health you are implementing.

Even though some people go a little extreme on cardio training, there are those of us who may, let's just say, not have that desire. I'm one of those people that doesn't innately get attached to cardio activities very easily. Sure, I can go out and run, but I'm usually not going to love it like someone who runs marathons all the time. I'm sure there are those of you like me that don't really love cardio. That's okay! I don't want you to have to create a love for it, but just create an obtainable habit for your health. However, don't let your previous experiences of cardio (maybe a PE class, sports, or other memories that made your fondness for cardio less than appealing) take away your drive to be active.

The Health Benefits

In 1953, a little while ago, a scary percentage was found out about US children. Over 55 percent of our children could not meet the minimum fitness and health requirements as compared to those in Europe. That was just in the 1950s! Can you just imagine how much worse it has become over the years? In the 1960s and 1970s, several expert panels were brought together to help develop and improve fitness standard recommendations. However, the issue was that those panels were focused mainly on comparing different exercise training regimens to prove cardiovascular fitness. Thankfully in the 1970s, a man by the name of Michael Pollock produced findings and an article titled "The Recommended Quantity and Quality of Exercise for Developing and Maintaining Fitness in Healthy Adults." Now not that you're rearing to go read this article; it basically explained the very first and effective guidelines for improving cardiorespiratory fitness, how to use large muscle groups, how long to work them, and how often. This article gave a whole new standard for adults and children alike and gave us the ideas of a more structured program to follow.

The great news that I'm sure you'll love to hear is that as time went on and research continued, it was found that significant health-related benefits could be achieved at lower levels of physical activity. Yay! So this meant that we didn't have to force our children or ourselves to go outside and run miles and miles to become healthier. We discovered that it was more beneficial, obtainable, and lifelong if we encouraged smaller and easier bouts of exercise for the general population. So when 1996 came around, Surgeon General's guidelines came out and explained the enormous benefits of physical activity. Their evidence was based on the benefits accumulated just from at least thirty minutes of moderate intensity on several days of the week. So all of this may interest you or may not, but I'll summarize with this: After those guidelines were published, more findings showed that the inclusion of muscular fitness, flexibility, and neuromotor fitness all played a wonderful part in improving health. So much so that finally in 2007, it was decided by the American College of Sports Medicine that physical activity needs to be required for the benefits that come from exercise, and the American Heart Association stated, "*All healthy adults aged 18–65 years need moderate-intensity aerobic physical activity for a minimum of 30 minutes on five days each week or vigorous-intensity aerobic activity for a minimum of 20 minutes on three days each week*" (Haskell, 1423).

So now what do you do? You have learned that over time we have figured out that we do indeed do cardio in our daily lives to achieve significant health benefits for the majority of our lives. Curious, isn't it, that we are just now figuring out how good exercise is for us when God created our bodies to be active and exercise from the beginning of time? I mean, He knew all along how well our bodies thrive when they are out getting the heart pumping. This is no surprise for God, but for all of us, well, let's just say that we're right on track to continue to prove God's existence through His creation. Cardio, my friends, has been carefully thought out and planned at the beginning of time.

So now that we know there are indeed health benefits, let me explain to you exactly what happens when we allow ourselves to introduce cardio into our lives:

» It lowers your risk of early mortality from all causes and even heart diseases and type 2 diabetes.

» It reduces the chance of death in all cases.

» You will increase your likelihood of increased habitual activities.

» Improvement in cardiovascular and respiratory function—everything works easier and faster.

» It will reduce your coronary artery disease risk factors—blood pressure will lower; cholesterol will be more manageable; insulin and glucose will be balanced.

» Cardio will decrease morbidity and mortality.

» It will also decrease your anxiety and depression, reduce the risk of falls and injuries in older persons, boost your feelings of well-being, improve the physical function and independent living in seniors, improve performance at work and recreational or sport activities, can help prevent or decrease limitations in older adults, and is a very effective type of therapy for chronic disease in seniors as well (Battista 2018, 417).

Really I could have made this list last forever. It is astounding how many benefits come from cardiorespiratory exercise. Again, it's as if God knew all along that we needed those health benefits, huh? So honestly, as you're sitting there thinking, *Why should I?* I think the real question is, "Why shouldn't you?" Only in very rare occasions are there situations where exercise will hinder your health and not improve it. But for the mass majority of us, I guarantee you that exercise and eating well *will* improve your life. Science shows it; God designed it, and I'm telling you that you have nothing to lose by taking on a healthier lifestyle. So maybe it's time to really ask yourself why you have strayed so far away from cardio or fitness in general. Let me remind you before you start thinking of running or super crazy cardio that will make you back out. As I will soon show you, you do not have to do insane cardio or fitness routines to be in good shape. People who choose those routes enjoy that kind of challenge, but not everyone (including myself) loves putting themselves through that kind of work. However, there are more enjoyable routes for you to go that will still enable you to improve your health and not have to go hardcore. Please, don't throw away the opportunity to become healthier just because it was hard before. Stick with me; let me show you what you can do. I think you'll find there's more than meets the eye than doing an elliptical for two hours for cardio.

Starting Cardiovascular Training

Let's start with some basics and talk about the basic cardio recommendations for adults:

Frequency—adults (eighteen to sixty-five years) need to be participating in at least five or more days a week of moderate exercise or three days or more of vigorous exercise. Or you can even do a combination of moderate and vigorous exercise and shoot for three to five days a week. If you don't know what your exercise level is, perform the talk test. If you can hold a conversation easily, you're probably doing mild exercise. If you can talk but are more breathy, you may be in the moderate range. And finally, if you cannot hold a conversation or talk, then you are performing at a vigorous intensity level.

Intensity—recommendations say that for most adults (unless you have a chronic condition, are a sedentary person, or have another underlying situation), then you should be practicing moderate and/or vigorous intensity. This range will be the most beneficial for those who are deconditioned and are desiring to get into better shape or lose weight.

Time—for adults, the general recommendation is 150 minutes a week of purposeful moderate exercise. Or you can do 75 minutes a week of vigorous exercise. And yes, you can still shoot to do a combination of moderate and vigorous exercise. Don't worry if you feel like 150 minutes a week is daunting. Not all of us are there yet, and it will take time to get to that point. Good news is that studies show that <20 minutes of exercise for people who are sedentary are still very beneficial. So wherever you are starting from, some exercise is better than none. And the more you can get used to it, the more you can build and the more results you will see.

Type—when focusing on cardiorespiratory exercise, the main goal is to pursue regular and purposeful exercises that will involve your major muscle groups.

Pattern—are you a very busy individual with little spare time? Good news! You can still get those great cardio benefits by doing several small sessions of cardio (an example would be ten minutes or less at a time) to accumulate to a total of thirty or more minutes a day. So if you have several small breaks in your workday, take those five to ten minutes to walk to the stairs. When your next break comes on, do the same thing or another cardio activity. However you do it, the great thing is that you can piece together your cardio segments however you like. If you're a very deconditioned individual, then shooting for less than ten-minute segments may favor you even more as you can adapt more easily to introduce consistent exercise.

Progression—this is one of the most important subjects people fail to include in their programs. You must progress your exercise volume by either adjusting your duration, how often, and/or the intensity at which you exercise. You need to make sure it's geared toward what your goal is for exercise, and you need to do your adjusting in small increments. Don't get to a level of thirty minutes a day of cardio and decide you want to push yourself, so you make it forty-five minutes a day. That's a large jump, and unless you know for a fact that you can continue that amount without fail for forever, don't burn yourself out.

170

Do small increments. Shoot for thirty-five minutes, and then after a month, then go for forty. It takes time for your body to progress, so don't push it overboard unless you're ready for that challenge and are willing to continue it for the long haul.

Cardiorespiratory endurance training refers to the ability of an individual to perform large muscle, repetitive, moderate-to high-intensity exercise for an extended period. The goal is to increase heart rate and respiration in order to place an appropriate physiological stress on the cardiorespiratory system.

Battista 2018

When you put that right amount of stress on your system, you enact what is called "overload." Overload is usually applied to muscular training but also to cardio training. When you overload your system (when you push it past its usual usage), it is one of the only ways to get beneficial adaptations in your cardiorespiratory endurance. What I'm trying to tell you is that if you don't get up and start trying, you will never improve your cardio or your fitness, for that matter. So yes, you do have to exercise to improve your health and fitness. Again, however, like I've said so many times before, there is no "one-size-fits-all" type of program. You have to find out what works for you to stay consistent. Now that you know the starting point for cardio, let's jump in and talk about how to create your own cardio plan that will be right for you.

Creating Your Own Program

When thinking of cardio, it should go without saying, but many don't know that you must start your workout off with a good warm-up of five to ten minutes. Then after your warm-up, you'll practice your endurance phase, and finally, you'll end with a cooldown. Please, please do not stretch before exercising. This is a practice that has been continued from exercise experts long ago that stretching reduces your chance of injury. Stretching can reduce injuries once you've cooled down. However, when you stretch before you exercise, you basically cool down your muscles and then force them to go right to exercising. There's a greater chance of injury when you force cold muscles to start performing. So, all in all, you must warm up first before your actual exercise program, and when all is said and done, you can do your stretching and cool down after.

Just to remind you how important a warm-up actually is, getting warm helps with the following: reducing the susceptibility of injury to muscles or joints, improving your joint range of motion, improving your muscular performance, and helping prevent a lack of oxygen (ischemia) to your heart muscle, which is very important to those who have any underlying heart conditions or heart complications. When putting together a warm-up, it doesn't have to be anything complex. Your goal of a warm-up is to literally raise your body temperature so that it's nice and "warm" so it's ready to exercise. When you do your warm-up, it should consist of low-level activities that are similar to what your actual endurance exercise will be. For example, if you're going to do a High Intensity Interval Training (HIIT) workout,

172

then whatever exercises are contained in your HITT you should do at a lower intensity in your warm-up. So if you have squats, jumping jacks, and, let's say, lunges, you should include all of those activities in your warm-up. This will prepare all of your muscles and joints to already move in those motions for your endurance phase. Honestly, I usually feel warm in about five minutes, but you need to listen to your own body. It may take you a full ten minutes or a little more to feel warm. Just make sure that you are. Let's talk about another example like going for a run. Do you just run to warm up for running? No. Instead, you need to do some fast-paced walking or in-place activities to warm up your knees, ankles, arms, and core. Also, as a good tidbit, any cardio exercise you're planning on doing, just YouTube a good warm-up. I guarantee there are hundreds of different running warm-ups that will get your heart pumping and get you ready.

For your endurance phase, the actual cardio exercise is very simple. Plan ahead a cardio exercise that you will perform the FITT principle too. Remember FITT stands for Frequency, Intensity, Time, and Type. So before you start at a solid thirty straight minutes of running, I suggest you try a couple of small cardio tests to see where you should start. Again, if you have any known health problems or concerns, you need to make sure and check with your doctor before starting up your own program. When you get the okay, do a couple of small tests to see where you are at. Try going for a mile walk. Can you do it easily, or are you out of breath? If a mile is too far, then try a half-mile. This walk test will tell you that if it's difficult, you're a beginner and need to start slow, which is perfectly fine! If you can jog for ten minutes without stopping, then try running a half-mile to a mile. Can you complete a full mile without stopping? If it's easy for you, then you're probably close to starting at a moderate intensity, but if you can't run the mile or half-mile, then I would still suggest starting at the beginning stage, again, which is perfectly fine. And for those of you that can run a long-distance or do most activities, for that matter, with ease, you're probably sitting more at a moderate to vigorous level. So once you've found your level, start at or even a little under your intensity. This way, it'll guarantee you don't go out too hard too fast.

Last but not least for your cardio workout is to do your cool down. Yes, you actually need to do your cool down, don't skip it as so many people do. I'll illuminate why it's so important for your cool down to take place: cooldowns allow your heart rate to slow down, your blood pressure and your breathing rate will return to normal, and it helps remove more lactic acid from your muscles that you produced during your endurance phase. When you put this all together, cooldowns will help your overall performance because your body will be given a chance to return to normal so that it can start healing from the endurance phase faster. Depending on how intense your workout was, you may need to do a longer cool down. The general suggestion is a ten-minute cooldown, but if you worked really hard, then you can take a fifteen or even twenty if you need to get your heart rate back down. While doing your cool down, it's suggested that you do half of the time, followed by stretching. So, for example, if you went for a run, then you should walk for five minutes and then stretch the last five minutes. If you are at the point where you're endurance phase is at a beginner level like brisk walking, then your cool down can be a little shorter and include less moving activity and more dynamic stretches.

Individualize Your Cardiovascular Workout

I wonder if a few of you who have been told their entire life the wrong information about exercise don't believe me that programing your own exercise program can be as simple as A, B, and C. Well, I'm telling the truth, and if you want to prove me wrong you go on current articles and journals, or get a degree in health and fitness or get your personal training certificate. But you don't need to. The whole point of this book was to basically condense and simplify all the information they teach us "health nerds" and share it to you all so that you finally have access to the simple keys to turning your life around. Sure, when you go to a personal trainer, or if you have ever gone before, you know they'll ask you some intense and personal questions about your current health. What do you eat, what your exercise looks like... so they can figure out how to create a plan for you. If we can just separate those two sentences that would be awesome! Does any of that sound familiar? It should! I've spent the majority of this book up to this point walking you through how to do all of that on your own. You may not be getting all the fancy, scientific equations we are taught to find out your exact target heart rate or your VO2max, which is the maximal amount of oxygen a person will use during exercise. Here's some more; I could try to interest you in finding out what your target VO2max is so that you know exactly how much oxygen you need to spend so you can hit that perfect amount of work every time. However, I don't think most of you are going to be interested or need that information to become healthier!

Here's the truth of the matter, God put it on my heart to write this book for the everyday people. He didn't ask me to write this book for those professional athletes that have to perform at that perfect level. I didn't feel like He was asking me to write a book about exercise science, which is what all of those fancy terms and equations boil into. I felt in my heart of hearts that God was asking me to write a book to share with you. Let me say that again for emphasis. You. I'm writing this book for you because there's not a book out there yet for you. There are hundreds upon hundreds of people who are far smarter than me that have written books to show people how to do those fancy tests and equations to find the exact science of why their body is doing it and how to make it perform better. How many books are written by some incredible doctors out there talking about how to make a professional athlete better or how to understand the inner workings of exercise in the body? So many! You can Google right now and find all the books you want that can explain better and dive further into the science of exercise, but that's not what I'm going to do. All I want to do, all I want to share, is my passion for finding the simple types of good and healthy exercise and eating that will allow you to live a better life for Christ. Because of that, yes, all of my information will be simple, and that's just how I want it.

So take a breath and realize it's okay for exercise to be easy. It's okay that you're not going to dedicate half of your life to planning out your routine, weighing out every single piece of food you consume, and spending hours upon hours in the gym. Those people who do that, congratulations to them that have the lifestyle they can pursue. I hope it gets them where they want to go. For the rest of us who have families, crazy schedules, and all of the above, this book's design is for you. Remember it's focused on making you your best for God, not the world. So yeah, it's going to be different. When you're looking at the cardio information I just gave you, I want you to consider one more very important concept that most people don't talk about enough. Your body works differently and reacts differently than anyone else's.

This honestly is probably one of the most exciting subjects for me to talk to you about because not many people like to talk about it! Just like my personality, I've always done things differently. First and foremost, remember God made you uniquely. *"Before I formed you in the womb I knew you, before you were born I set you apart..."* (Jeremiah 1:5). God knew exactly what He was making when He made your body. It's perfect like we've discussed before. You have different abilities, talents, personalities, quirks, all of the above. So your body is different too. It makes sense that there's no cookie-cutter way for all body types, huh? Strange, the fitness industry hardly addresses that. So let's just dive right into what I'm trying to tell you.

If you have the time in your schedule to pursue 150 minutes a week of cardio, and oh yeah, don't forget some resistance training two to three times a week, and of course, who could forget about flexibility, then go right for it! If you are so motivated to take those proven numbers to the utmost height and work your little behind off, then do it! You will see some amazing results with your life and overall health, I guarantee you. However, what about the parents with several kids run-

177

ning around? What about the college kids that are so busy with school, work, and learning how to be adults? What about the businessman or woman that has become so successful but now can't imagine how to fit in time for their personal health? What about the grandparents that are trying to fit in every activity their grandkids have, plus their social life and other events? And I know I missed some situations, but you are all included in this list as well. Here's the thing, even though those numbers and "how tos" that I shared with you are the proven, real-deal thing, they aren't the most practical, are they?

Let me tell you that I know the fitness industry will not tell you what I'm about to. The fitness industry has the numbers and keys to help you get healthier but won't share them because scams make more money, and so do expensive personal trainers. The industry has actual numbers and equations for you to plug in about your body to get those results you want, but unless you pay some money to learn about them, then you won't find it. Even if you can get ahold of those numbers, they won't guarantee they will work with your lifestyle. And lastly, the industry has never understood one very important aspect; we are all humans with busy lives and budgets. Common sense (which is a very rare trait today) is the real winner when it comes to planning out your exercise life. Plan your activities with the right goals (our godly goals we've discussed). See how much time you *realistically* can put towards exercise a week without burning out. Make slow adjustments over time, and don't go so hard that you'll make yourself sick of exercise or eating well. Simple, right? That's exactly what I've been trying to tell you.

Here are my tips and tricks for how to fit your cardio in for those busy lifestylers and just starting outers:

» Busy lifestyles: If you only have ten to fifteen minutes, maybe, a day, then I would suggest you look into a HIIT workout program. You can find simple, short workouts that can fit in even with the busiest schedules. You can YouTube and find hundreds that are without equipment, make no noise, for advanced or beginner, stylized for preference like dance or boot camp, and even short five to eight minutes. Think of all of those breaks you may get in your day. Can you find five, ten, or fifteen minutes to squeeze in a program? Moms, think about naptime. You could try the "no noise" HIITs to fit in a quick workout. Whatever your situation may be, I can guarantee that you can find a HIIT that can work for you if you're willing to try. If you go the HIIT route, I suggest doing HIITs three to four times a week. You can pursue more, but as I have learned from experience, they're very easy to burn out on quickly. Pace yourself with different styles and varieties, lengths, and intensities. Change it up if you have time one day and do a different exercise like Zumba or Pilates. Here's an example program I would suggest for you to try:

» Fifteen-minute HIIT two to four times a week, ten to fifteen minutes of resistance training two to three times a week, flexibility/yoga two to three times a week.

» Sounds like too much? Think about it this way. Fit your cardio in during the day or before you start your day.

Then on the days when you don't have cardio, fit in your quick resistance training exercises. Then on days off, right before you go to bed or right as you wake up, do a short yoga program to get some flexibility in your day. Again, if you're willing to try, I know you'll find time to make this fit. The fact of the matter is you just have to be willing to try, fail, and try again until you find the pattern that works the best for you.

» Just starting out: If you're a beginner with exercise and the thought is intimidating to you, do not fret. I've been doing exercise programs for a long time, and still, the thought of new ones or harder ones makes me nervous. It's okay to be nervous, but all I want you to do is promise me you'll try and stick with it. Again, remember it takes about three months to make a habit stick, so give yourself the goal of three months of activity, and I think you'll see at those three months how much has changed for the better. Maybe you're a nervous workout person like me, or maybe due to health conditions, you need to take it slow. Whatever it is, slow and steady wins the race in the end. So for your situation, I would suggest doing small time intervals of only ten to fifteen minutes, maybe twenty if you're feeling up to it. Do small and easy workouts that you can actually enjoy instead of making yourself suffer. Suffering through workout after workout will only make you dislike exercise more, which is the exact opposite of what I want for you. Do activities you can do like walking, maybe higher paced yoga, cycling, stairs, or whatever you like best. Google some ideas if you need to. Here's my suggestion for your program:

» Ten to fifteen minutes of cardio five to six times a week, resistance training two to three times a week, and flexibility two to three times a week.

  » Again, don't stress if this is a lot compared to your normal. Start slow. Just start out for two weeks with your cardio. Then when the cardio is becoming easier and more maintainable, include an easy resistance program. And finally, start slipping in a day or two of easy flexibility training. Before you know it, you can have all the necessary areas of training in your schedule, and it won't be an overload.

So there you are, very simplified workout programs for even those different lifestyles. Yes, if you calculate those numbers, they won't all add up to 150 minutes a week. Well, you're right. You're not meeting those exact standards. But the numbers I provided are doing something; they are getting you started. Down the line, once you've created a habit of exercising, and I pray you enjoy it more than you used to, you will be at a point where you can progress in your intensity to meet those 75 minutes a week of vigorous exercise or maybe have found time in your life to shoot for the 150 minutes. But if you don't, that's okay too. What is the most important here is for you to find out what works for your body. Some of you may try these simple programs and by month three start to lose pounds and see differences. Some of you may see small changes but not a lot. And some of you may not see any change at all. Change or no change, difference or no difference, you will find out more about your body than you will if you just become a couch potato. Once you add in nutrition, you will also have to learn how to balance that with exercise to see the results you are striving for. In the end, this is all about consistency, balance, and modification. As you see how your body does, modify what feels and works better. As your body gets stronger and healthier, progress. And as you learn how to adapt to this new lifestyle of activity and healthier eating, learn to balance it in your life. That's it. There's not much more that I can suggest to you from here. All you can do is trust that God will give you the strength for the right goals, and He will give you the ability to pursue them.

Chapter 12

FACTS OF RESISTANCE PROGRAMS

*For every creature of God is good, and nothing to be refused,
if it be received with thanksgiving: For it is sanctified by the
word of God and prayer. If though put the brethren in remem-
brance of these things, thou shalt be a good minister of Jesus
Christ, nourished up in the words of faith and of good doctrine, whereunto thou hast attained. But refuse profane and
old wives' fables, and exercise thyself rather unto godliness.
For bodily exercise profiteth little: but godliness is profitable
unto all things, having promise of the life that now is, and of
that which is to come. This is a faithful saying and worthy of
all acceptance.*

1 Timothy 4:4–9

The section of 1 Timothy that you read is a very powerful passage,
as it contains so many hidden jewels that Paul is writing to us
to grow and learn from. First and foremost, Paul starts off in verses
1–5 by telling people about false teachers that are currently deceiving believers into thinking that all physical matters are evil. The false

teachers claim that things like eating, drinking, and even things like marriage are evil because they are physical.

It would be a very hard life if we believed what the false teachers said was true and tried to abstain from eating, drinking, and wonderful blessings like marriage. I don't think even for a second it makes sense because if God created the body to hunger, to be thirsty, then surely He meant for us to satisfy those feelings. Even when it comes to marriage, He created that as a blessing to us as well to have a small taste of what it means when the Lamb will come for His bride, the church. Also, a marriage between the Savior and ourselves.

Paul, thankfully, starts then to explain that those false teachers are wrong because, "*For every creature of God is good, and nothing to be refused, if it be received with thanksgiving.*" Paul is basically explaining that anything created by God is good and should not be rejected. God has given us tools to be used with a thankful heart, which is the one stipulation Paul mentions in verse 4. Can we please just take a minute to appreciate that God knew from the very first moment in our existence that we needed certain physical activities to maintain our health? He knew we would need to be active in the beginning of the creation of the world to survive. He also knew that after thousands and thousands of years, we would *still* need physical activities to help us. But the sad fact is that we are a detriment to our own health. However, we can be grateful for an all-knowing God that knows what we need and has provided us a way to reap those benefits.

My point in mentioning those benefits is to pair up with the fact that Paul is reminding us that using our bodies for God is good, and the benefits point out that God has created several blessings from using our bodies well. So as you start down this road of resistance training, just remember that no matter what type, how often, or any of the "hows," just do them for God.

So this wonderful explanation Paul gives us only makes me wonder if God knew that we would be tempted to use our bodies for the wrong purposes. It is true that our bodies are sinful vessels that were tainted from the first day with Adam and Eve, but that doesn't mean they can't serve God when we have the right heart to use them. Just as we talked extensively in the first half of this book about using your body for God, we now jump into the part where we justify the idea that when our hearts are right with God, we can indeed use our bodies in the physical sense for God. Now is the time to jump in and show you how to actually start using the different areas of fitness to make you a living sacrifice, starting with resistance training.

Health Benefits of Resistance Programs

So to start off here, I want to make you aware of how beneficial resistance training can be. Now, when I say resistance training, I'm talking about basically a program that specifically focuses on some kind of bone-loading activity. Now, hear me when I say this: when I talk about lifting weights, I'm not going to tell you that each and every one of you needs to go out and start the process of becoming a bodybuilder. Weight training is great for you if it's: body weight training, light weights, powerlifting, Olympic lifting, and all the hundreds of ways that are out there for you to lift weights. The point is, no matter what route you choose, it is all very good for you. And to start that off, you should know that weight lifting makes you physically stronger, makes your bones stronger, lowers your risks of falls and injuries, promotes greater flexibility and mobility, and can help better brain function.

Now the physical benefits of weight training are outstanding, and if you don't currently practice weight training, then I highly encourage you to do so because it will only improve your quality of life. However, I want to remind you that *"For bodily exercise profiteth little: but godliness is profitable unto all things, having promise of the life that now is, and of that which is to come. This is a faithful saying and worthy of all acceptance."* Paul reminds us and warns us that even though our bodies were made by God to be used for God is good, we need to be careful to not let that focus turn into an obsession. Paul specifically states that bodily exercise is good but only a little when compared to the whole aspect of God. So when you want to start your resistance program, don't forget where your *real strength* comes from. I want to remind you to keep your priorities straight, don't let this world mold you. For example, I was looking up the best benefits of resistance training, and there are the typical ones I already mentioned, some good ones I will tie in later, but then there are the more "worldly" items like: "You'll get more toned. You'll have better confidence in yourself because you'll look better. Helps you look leaner." Don't get me wrong; lifting can help you feel more confident and help you lose weight. However, the mindset behind those aspirations is what is dangerous. Don't get caught up in what the world tries to motivate you by. Focus on building this body, though it will never equal God's strength, and build it to be strong for *His uses.*

Another great reason to pursue weight lifting is that it can burn calories efficiently, help you lose weight, improve heart health, manage your blood sugar levels, boosts your mood, and improve brain health. Now, these wonderful health benefits will apply to you no matter what age you are. From children to seniors, weight lifting is so good for you. It's actually funny if you think about it; God designed our bodies to be able to lift weight in amazing ways all through our lives, yet now we've gotten to a point where we don't do any lifting. And what's happened now that we don't use a gift from God? We see health issues all over the place popping up. But when we pursue the benefits, it's almost uncanny to think how good it is for us, but God knew that all along. We just happened to be a little slow on the uptake to realize that maybe God designed us to do it for a reason because He knew we needed it. Wow, I mean, I know that humans are pretty slow, but when things like this pop up, I can just imagine God sitting there saying, "Yes, it's that good for you. That's why I created it for you to do."

Starting the Weightlifting Process

Now it's time to jump and discuss the basics of resistance training for adults.

Muscular fitness includes both muscular strength and muscular endurance. Muscular strength refers to the ability of a muscle or a muscle group to exert force. Muscular endurance

187

refers to the ability of a muscle or muscle group to continue to perform without fatigue, (i.e., repeated contractions or to sustain a contraction.). To improve muscular fitness, the muscles must be exposed to an overload (stress beyond the typical activity). This is done via resistance training.

Battista 2018, 376

So as the *ACSM's Resource for the Personal Trainer* states, basically, you need to start your resistance program by exposing various muscles to different forces that they have to overcome. Whether you want to focus on building endurance-type of muscles or more of a strength-based muscle, you need to use a heavier weight than what your current muscles can lift. We're going to call your current state the "original" state, and when you lift heavier, it will be referred to as the "working" state.

So your original state may be at a minimal weight lifting ability. That's okay! We all have to start somewhere, and trust me, starting is the hardest thing to do. But if you can allow yourself to get around all the previous misconceptions about lifting and maybe some insecurities you have, I promise you that in the future, you will be so thankful you did start. Remember God's given you these goods to use! Don't let those goods just sit around and further your career as a couch potato. Today is the day you need to get up and decide it's time for your original state to put in a little work.

I also want to put a quick word in here for those who don't like the idea of weight lifting because they're afraid they'll become too bulky.

Let me just set the facts straight here; lifting does not make you bulky. Only if you're doing a crazy amount of weights every day and eating an insane amount of food, plus your goal is to get (as the kids say nowadays) as "swol" as possible, then you can get bulky. It's actually really hard to get bulked up because you have to work so consistently and eat a lot more calories to make it happen. It doesn't happen overnight either. It takes people years to get the bulk they want. So rest assured, you starting out with a simple weight lifting program won't turn you into the next Dwayne Johnson. Lifting, however, will help tone muscles, boost your metabolism so it burns calories faster, helps you become more defined, and will obviously make you stronger.

So for those of you that may need to start at the beginning with lifting weights, pay close attention. I don't want you to go straight to the gym and start busting out super hard weights hoping that will pay off. Actually, if you go that route, you're more likely to injure yourself and backtrack from where you are now. It takes time and slow progression to increase your strength. Let me put it like this: If you wanted to start running a marathon (why you would want to is beyond me because it sounds like death, but if you did), you wouldn't go straight out of your house with no training under your belt and try to run the full twenty-six point two miles, would you? I would hope you wouldn't. If you can, then my goodness, good for you. But the fact of the matter is you are more likely going to cause some serious injury to your body. The same is true for weight lifting. You have to start low and slow and build from there. To start you off, I want to introduce a concept that is vital to your exercise journey, the FITT Principle. The

"F" stands for frequency, "I" for intensity, the first "T" for time, and the last "T" for type. These are all the areas you need to find out for your program to be successful.

Frequency: Adults (eighteen to sixty-five years) need to be lifting at least two to three times a week. For those of you that are sixty and up, you also are recommended to lift two to three times but at a lower intensity. Also, you may not be physically in a position yet to lift that much, so if that's the case, then start with only lifting one to two times a week. While lifting, you need to target the *six major muscle groups: hips and legs, chest, back, shoulders, low back, and abdominals.*

All of those muscle groups have been shown to be the most vital to exercise consistently, and that's been proved by amazing scientists. Those six muscle groups are the largest types of muscles you have in your system, and to grow and give yourself a good baseline of muscular fitness, you need to build those ones first. Specific muscles like biceps, triceps, trapeziums, and the like are important but can wait to be focused on specifically. More than likely, your big muscle workouts will target those smaller ones, just not quite as intense as a specific exercise for them. Don't be disheartened if you really want those big biceps or shoulder muscles. They'll come with time. Like I've said from the beginning, you have to put in the work to have those results in the long run but stick with it. Now I feel like, at this point, you may be thinking, That's it? Yes, actually, for the basic lifting component. It doesn't take a rocket scientist or super expensive personal trainer to show you this magic method. The point is, if you start right and target the right areas, you'll be making leaps and bounds.

Intensity: "*Intensity of resistance training is inversely related to the number of repetitions: with higher resistance, the number of repetitions will be fewer. To improve muscular fitness, typically 8–12 repetitions per set are completed, at an intensity of between 60–80%...*" (Battista 2018). This is saying that you need to lift at a certain level of difficulty to obtain results. You don't need to go all out to where you can't even feel your arms or legs, but you have to push yourself a little past your comfort level. For example, if you can bicep curl five pounds easily for three reps of ten sets, I would encourage you to try ten-pound weights. Technique is key, so you do the amount of repetitions that you can do correctly and then go back to your five pounds. That added *difficulty* will only progress you, and before you know it, you can do all the sets with the ten pounds.

When talking about the percentage of your life, your weight is about 60 percent to 80 percent of your max amount that you could possibly lift. So, for example, if you could only do a couple of body weight squats, then I would recommend that you focus on doing eight to twelve half squats, focusing on slow and controlled movements that will build your baseline muscle. This way, you're working a little past 50 percent of your muscle capacity, but I wouldn't be having you go all out and completely kill your muscles after three full squats.

Here's another example. Back in college, I really wanted to be able to do pull-ups. I was dating my to-be husband at the time, and he was ridiculously good at them, and I could barely do one, maybe two. I also had this ambition of wanting to do more than the average woman because it made me feel tough and strong. I had a little bit of

191

an ego with lifting back in college, that I hate to admit, but thankfully God is working on my pride to be put in a better place. I still struggle with my pride for wanting to be strong for sure, but I'm a lot better than I used to be. Anyways, for several reasons, I was determined to get better at pull-ups. I started using the assisted pull-up machine in the gym almost every day. At first, I was so hard on myself and frustrated that I could not really do a strict pull-up. I kept pushing myself harder and harder, just waiting to see the results. Truth of the matter was, however, that I pushed the same muscles over and over again that instead of seeing strength build in my upper body, I felt exhausted, sore, unmotivated, and honestly more weak doing pull-ups than when I first started.

If I had been smart back then, commonly a fault of mine, I would have listened to my body and perhaps, this is just me thinking out loud, that my body was tired. Hm, what a concept. I pushed those muscles to the extreme that instead of improving and getting stronger, those muscles were completely worn out. If we talk about the anatomy of the muscle and what happens when you build muscle, the weight you lift actually tears your current muscle, next you feel sore, which is your body slowly building back up your muscle, which in turn is actually making your muscle stronger by helping it adapt over the stimulation you just gave it. So I never rested, and so my muscles could never fully recover. It's amazing I actually didn't hurt something.

Time: Otherwise as duration. It's basically how long you are going to work out. When it comes to cardio, it tends to be a little more straightforward. When it comes to resistance training, however, it's a little different. *"Total time will vary with the program, in particular if a whole body approach is used or if a split program targeting different muscles groups on separate days is applied"* (Battista 2018, 363). Now when it comes to adults, you should focus on training at least two to four sets (a set is a term for a set of repetitions, e.g., three sets of eight reps) and then implement rest intervals of two to three minutes in between lifts. Also, it's important to know that yes, four sets can be better than just two, but if you're a novice, take care in knowing that even one set per exercise will improve muscular strength.

Type: The type of mode you are going to do. When I say mode, I mean free weights, machines that can be stacked weights, or even pneumatic resistance; you can do resistance bands or cords and, lastly, body weight. All of these "types" of resistance training are good for you; there's not one that's better than the other. Remember our focus is to build muscle and help your body get into a healthier and stronger state. If you wanted to go the body-building route, then you would obviously need to focus more on stacked weights and machines. So whatever your goal is, match the type of mode to it. The main thing you must do when you pick your mode is make sure you include *"…multijoint (e.g., bench press, leg press) as well as potentially single-joint (e.g., biceps curl, quadriceps extension) exercises."* This statement from the standards of ACSM basically says that working your joints either one at a time or enacting several for one lift is very important and healthy for building strong joints. Next, you need to ensure opposing muscle groups, agonists and antagonists, are included in order to prevent muscle imbalances. For example, including lower back extensions and abdominal crunches to strengthen both the lower back and the abdomen will provide for muscle balance. All that statement meant that you need to work all the muscles of that limb to prevent an imbalance. So, for instance, in your legs, you have those muscles in the front part of your leg, your quadriceps, and also the muscles in the back, which are your hamstrings. Those are opposing muscles, and if you were to build one more than the other, it would cause different issues to arise in your joints and hips and a risk of injury to weaker muscles. So when you work your upper body, make sure to work those biceps and triceps. Work those abdominals and your upper and lower back.

Progression: Resistance training progression is quite simple. As you get stronger, include one of four different ways to progress yourself, the weight of resistance (body weight, dumbbell, barbell, weighted vest, etc.), the amount of repetitions you do (more reps equal a variety of endurance training), amount of sets (this will focus on your strength and hypertrophy of your muscles), and finally how powerfully you perform them (this works on the power of your muscles). Whatever your goals are, whether it's to increase your strength or maybe better your endurance, make sure you go the route that will be most beneficial to your goals. You must progress, however, because if you don't, you'll only plateau, which will make you frustrated that you're not seeing any progress. My rule of thumb is to start to increase the difficulty when you notice that you can perform all your sets and reps with ease. Usually, this takes anywhere from four to twelve weeks, depending on your fitness level and experience. If you want to stay where you are, continue to do the exercises you have done to get you to that point. If you just stop, you will lose your progress. You must maintain at least once a week of the same intensity of exercise to keep what you've built.

Rest: The amount of time to rest in between your sets as well as time to rest your muscles from your workouts. This is a commonly overlooked area that many people don't take seriously. It can actually be the hindrance in a lot of people not seeing results because their bodies just aren't getting enough rest to recover. For the rest between sets, you need to do a minimum of a minute up to three minutes. The reason for this rest time (even though it's hard sometimes to weigh when you're "in the mode") is to allow the muscle(s) time to rest so that when you do your next set, you can perform it at the same intensity you did the first couple sets. If you don't rest, you'll be worn out by set two or three and just basically limping through the rest of your reps, which won't challenge your muscles. However, by just implementing some rest time, your muscles will get the chance to be worked at the same intensity every set, which will help you see more results down the line. When it comes to rest between workouts, the recommendation is to allow at least forty-eight hours of rest for the muscle group you just worked. When you lift, you tear your muscle (that is why it feels "sore"), and it takes up to forty-eight hours for your body to build it back. If you continue to lift and not rest, you could either put yourself at risk for serious injury or never grow your muscle at all because it's too strained. Rest is vital!

So now that you know about the FITT principles of resistance training, you have the keys to your own fitness endeavors. Like I've been saying, there's no magic potion or trick that professionals know about getting you in shape. It comes down to discipline, consistency, and the knowledge of starting out safely and the right way. As you go on in your program, remember to progress your weight and your intensity. Rule of thumb, if it's starting to get really easy and you've stopped seeing any results, it's time to think about upping it up. However, if you're happy where you are at, then just remember you need to maintain your intensity level and weight to keep what you've gained. Also, remember only what you are working will grow, so make sure you're challenging your body in different areas and ways to vary what all is getting worked.

One last thing. There is a lot of information I didn't cover about resistance training because I would have to write my own mini-book about it to explain it all. I would encourage you to take the time to do some good research on your own time about lifting techniques. This is where a lot of people tend to struggle because they either skip this and lift improperly, which leads to injury, or are too shy to try and lift when they don't really know what to do. An easy hack to this is Google. No joke. With all the different fitness gurus in the world, everyone and their mom have a website or video dedicated to showing you the right form to perform any exercise. So when you find your program, take the time to look up each exercise to make sure you are performing them correctly. It may seem silly, but it's actually vital to work your muscles the best way and to keep yourself from injury and have the best results.

I want to give you an example of how to approach an exercise, learn how to do it properly, and then put it into action. Let's talk about squats, as it is a popular exercise that scares people. No matter what weight you decide, whether it's strictly body weight, dumbbells, or even using a barbell, you must learn the form first. This is where Google comes into play. First, you need to learn the key phrases for when you squat:

1. Feet a little wider than shoulder-width apart.

2. Toes slightly angled away from your body.

3. Chest up and squat down by hinging at the hips and pushing your glutes back like you're sitting in a chair. You don't want your knees to go over your toes, which is a telltale if you're correctly squatting or not.

4. You should squat as low as you can to start, but then as you progress, you should be able to get your thighs down to parallel with the floor.

5. Your knees should stay pointed out as you squat down, and don't let them buckle when you push back up.

6. Lastly, don't lock your knees when you come up from the squat. Keep them nice and loose.

This may sound confusing to you, so Google it. There are a million fitness coaches that will teach you the perfect way to squat to keep you safe and help you feel comfortable doing it on your own. Even if you have to start really slow with no weight, do it that way so that you can make sure you're doing each exercise perfectly. Practice honestly does make perfect when it comes to resistance training.

Chapter 13

FACTS OF FLEXIBILITY PROGRAMS

"The Lord knows those who are his," and, "everyone who confesses the name of the Lord must turn away from wickedness." In a large house there are articles not only of gold and silver, but also of wood and clay; some are for special purposes and some for common use. Those who cleanse themselves from the latter will be instruments for special purposes, made holy, useful to the Master and prepared to do any good work. Flee the evil desires of youth and pursue righteousness, faith, love and peace, along with those who call on the Lord out of a pure heart.

2 Timothy 2:19–22

Again we are reminded by Paul's writing when he's imprisoned in Rome, writing to Timothy, that it is important for Christians to live godly. We are to throw away our desires and temptations of this world and cleanse ourselves to be used for God's will. Just as Paul gives us the visual of different items that can be used for common or special purposes, he informs us that only through cleansing ourselves can we be made holy and used for God's special purposes. He then continues to instruct us to "flee" our temptations and pursue godly things like righteousness, faith, love, and peace. These verses are kind of similar to someone tossing a bucket of cold water on you. It's an awakening, as we realize that only when we clean ourselves of worldly things can God truly use us as He intended. Let me ask you this, have you been making yourself, your vessel, ready to be used for God or for this world?

Kind of an interesting passage to use when we're about to talk about flexibility, huh? Actually, I thought it was quite appropriate since the age of flexibility has suddenly become revolved around the tightest yoga pants and who can bend the farthest. I want to remind you all of something. God designed us to have the ability to be flexible. He knew that we would need the ability to be flexible and increase it if our situation needed it. So when you want to pursue a good flexibility program, I want to encourage you not to pursue it for what the world has made it out to be. You don't have to have super tight leggings or bend provocatively around others for them to see. Do it because you want to preserve good health and be ready to serve Him for whatever is down the road.

Is Flexibility Important?

Have you ever watched a baby play with its own feet? When babies get more motor skills, they soon discover their own feet and will grab them and start to play a type of tug of war with their own feet. Babies are super flexible. I mean, think about it, while lying on the floor, can you just reach down and grab your foot and bring it clear up to your mouth? What about both feet at the same time? I try to practice flexibility, and I still can't do some movements that babies can do. They're incredibly flexible!

Babies actually have more bones in their bodies than adults have. When born, babies have 300 bones, whereas a regular adult will only have 206 bones. All of the new babies' bones are joined together by flexible cartilage, which makes it easy for them to bend as they do, and most bones have not fused together yet like adults have, which makes them harder and stronger. I can't help but wonder why God designed babies to be so flexible. Well, for one, He knew that those babies needed to be flexible, as they grew in a very small space and came into the world through yet another small space. As those babies grow, they need that flexibility to allow big changes to constantly be growing in their own bodies. They also need to be flexible as they start to move and develop more motor skills, as it will allow their bodies to adjust to their constant movement. However, once those babies finally reach adulthood, suddenly that flexibility isn't quite as prevalent anymore.

As we age, our flexibility decreases, and more of us are unaware that we should be practicing flexibility. Why is that? Why does flexibility decrease as we age? Well, quite simply, it's because of a couple of reasons:

» Our tissue changes—the tissue around our joints starts to thicken, which can decrease our range of motion.

» We gain/lose fat and muscle—when people gain a lot of weight or a lot of muscle, sometimes the extra "stuff," if you will, can make it harder to move. Also, on the flip side, as we start to lose muscle as we get older, we can lose some of the vital muscle and ease of movement that helps us stay flexible.

» No activity or exercise—while there are some biological factors that subtract our flexibility, a lot of inactivity will actually cause a more prevalent cause of inflexibility. When someone is inactive, their muscles and joints will become still from lack of use which limits mobility.

» Gender—it's true; studies show that women are naturally more flexible than men due to different patterns of skeletal structure, hormonal differences, and types of connective tissue.

Basically, the less we move, the poorer we take care of our bodies, the more flexibility we will lose. Now maybe you're someone that could really care less if they can touch their toes or not. I'm not talking about just touching your toes. I'm talking about having the ability to bend over to put your shoes on, pull a shirt over your head, or even being able to get down on the ground without assistance. I'm talking about your daily activities that can either be improved with good flexibility or can be considerably harder if you become inflexible. Sure, now you may be young and not think about it as much. But as you age, you'll start to feel a change as it suddenly becomes hard to do tasks that weren't hard before.

The good news is that becoming inflexible is not a permanent thing. The more inflexible you are, the longer it will take to become flexible, but it's worth the time spent to reverse the situation.

Health Benefits of Flexibility

Benefits of flexibility:

» You will have an improved range of motion in the joints you practice on.

» Your ability to daily activities will be considerably easier.

» Risks of flexibility:

» If you become very flexible, you can run the risk of joint hypermobility, which is stretching to an extreme range of motion that can cause injuries.

» Flexibility is not a one-time fix-all. You have to continue stretching constantly to keep the benefits of flexibility; otherwise, it will decrease.

So unless you're a professional gymnast or another occupation where you have to do an intense range of motions every day, your risk of injuring yourself is very low through flexibility. For most of us, we just need to practice getting average flexibility back in our bodies so we can move easier and keep our mobility. And yes, you do have to continue to practice your flexibility to maintain it, but the good news is that you only need to practice two to three times a week to really make an impact and get the results. Unless your goals are to be able to do the splits, then the average flexibility plan will serve you perfectly well. Remember, flexibility is vitally important to do as we age so we can keep our joint mobility and keep moving like we want to.

Starting Your Flexibility Plan

You may have noticed that flexibility is a lot more simple than resistance training or cardiovascular training. It's true; flexibility is not complex, which is why it should be easy for you to implement it into your weekly routine. It may be a simple and easy concept, but it's still very important to include. If you design a wonderful workout program, really starting to get those good habits in to change your lifestyle but don't include flexibility, I promise you that you'll discover how much you'll be limited. Just think of those big bodybuilders who work so hard to get so big, but most of them don't practice flexibility. Yes, when you get bigger than average muscle mass, it does tend to limit some mobility anyways, but when you don't stretch and make it a habit, you'll find that you'll be stiff and have little range of motion. Same situation could go to a marathon runner who never stretches on a consistent basis. They may be able to run mile after mile, but their body will be stiff and immobile if they don't practice opening up their joints. It does help with performance in the end, and it improves your lifestyle.

So as you're wanting to include stretching in your weekly plan, the first step you need to decide is what type of stretching fits your goals and what type you enjoy the most. Don't pick an intense flexibility program because you think it could help you get where you need to be faster because, again, you won't stick with it if it becomes a really hard "focused" program. Instead, pick a type that is relaxing and enjoyable for you. Slowly start with easy stretches and increase your stretch as time goes on. The same rules apply to stretching as they do to cardio and resistance training.

There are five basic types of stretching that you can pursue: static stretching, dynamic stretching, PNF, passive stretching, and ballistic stretching.

1. Static—the most common type of stretching that people use to improve their flexibility. Basically, this type of stretching consists of slow movement to minor discomfort, and then you hold the stretch.

    a. Target all your major muscle groups and perform stretches two to three times a week; for the general population, you should hold your stretch ten to thirty seconds, and for older adults, you should hold for thirty to sixty seconds. Repeat the hold and stretch two to four times so you can get a total of sixty seconds for each exercise.

2. Dynamic—this type of stretching is much more active, as you're making your body move through a controlled range of motions while increasing the reach and speed. These types of stretches are usually a part of the "warm-up" phase before your endurance workout, as it is a "hot" type of stretching that gets your heart pumping, whereas static will be more like a "cool" stretch and more appropriate to include during cool down.

    a. Again, target all muscle groups, start gradually with a small

205

range of motion, and progress to a larger range; you should repeat each activity at least five to twelve times.

3. PNF (Proprioceptive Neuromuscular Facilitation)—this mouth of a stretching style is a more uncommonly used structure, as it is more difficult. PNF stretching really produces a big stretch that is challenging and is usually associated with athletes or individuals with high flexibility goals. You perform a PNF stretch by stretching a muscle, contracting the muscle against a force, and then stretching it again. This stretching also tends to require a trainer or an experienced helper with the stretch. For example, you're lying on your back, one leg on the ground, and the other is straight in the air while being pushed back towards your torso. To do a PNF stretch, you would allow your helper to push your leg as far back to your torso as you can go, holding the stretch for ten to thirty seconds. Then you relax your leg, and your helper holds your straight leg up in a neutral position, and you push (contract your muscle) against them. You contract your muscle for three to six seconds at about a 20 to 75 percent intensity and then relax. After contraction, you allow your helper to push your leg back into the original stretch one more time, and this time you'll be able to stretch further than before. This method of stretching is most effective with assistance, and you should be more cautious, as it is easier to cause injury if you're not listening to how your body responds.

   a. Same as before, target all muscle groups and practice this stretching two to three times a week, educate yourself properly with technique before pursuing, and perform after your body is warmed up. I suggest using it during your cool down.

4. Passive—this is personally one of my favorite types of stretching because it's really relaxing. I call passive stretching "partner stretching." When you passively stretch, you are not actively involved in your stretch. Your partner will hold a stretching apparatus like a strap or a limb like your arm to help you get a deep stretch.

   a. Follow the static stretching protocol; best used during cool down.

5. Ballistic—this was a common type of stretching in the '80s when "bouncing" was very popular in exercise. It is still a very useful type of stretching today but is more active. You use a "bounce" or a "jerky" movement to increase your range of movement. An example would be you're trying to touch your toes, so you include a light bounce in your torso to increase your stretch to your toes each time. This practice is not very common for the general population but more so for those in rehabilitation that need to practice an explosive movement. The possibility of tissue injury is higher with ballistic stretching, so it is suggested to have an experienced trainer or take instruction for proper form before trying.

   a. When designing a program here, you need to determine the activity-specific needs for your goals. Again, not suggested for the general population unless you have goals that include ballistic skills.

Those are your choices to choose from when it comes to flexibility training. Yes, you can pursue things like yoga, which is a combination of static and dynamic stretches, but the main idea is to pursue which one fits your goals the best. The general suggestion is to practice two to three times a week, but if that amount is not effective toward your goals, then modify it to fit you better. It is suggested that every four to six weeks, you test and record your current flexibility by a goniometer to measure any change in your range of motion (or just have an advanced stretch you try to see how much you're gaining). Once you pick a style, then the next thing is to make sure and practice stretches for all muscle groups:

>> neck
>> shoulders
>> chest
>> arms
>> back
>> torso
>> hips
>> thigh (anterior and posterior)
>> calves

The easiest way I can suggest for you to design your program is to Google stretches for each of these areas and find stretches that feel good for all of them. Don't pick exercises that cause you any immediate pain. Stretches should only produce a slight discomfort, so if you experience pain, then stop that exercise immediately. If something is hurting, then it would be beneficial to see your doctor before continuing to stretch that muscle. As you grow in your stretching, make sure you progress slowly with the length of your stretch. As you get more flexible, try other stretches that can challenge your range of motion more, or if you meet your goals, then continue to stretch those exercises consistently so that you keep your progress.

This should go without saying; as you know, I'm a stickler for form, but make sure when you stretch that you are following the precise form for that exercise. It won't do you any good to do them poorly and cause yourself an injury.

So now you know the types, how long, and the precautions. It's time to get out there and start thinking about what you want with your range of motion. Google or YouTube different stretching programs and see if any fit to your liking. Google popular stretching programs for people with back pain, leg pain, inflexibility, or whatever hindrance you are experiencing. I promise that after you implement a flexibility plan, you will feel a huge difference in your body. That desk job that makes your back hurt? Try stretching consistently; you'll discover the amazing differences one can make when one gets their body stretching.

A quick note for those who may have health concerns for flexibility like arthritis, muscular imbalances, osteoporosis, or hip fractures or replacements. First and foremost, talk to your doctor to see if he suggests starting a flexibility program right now. If you're ready and safe to start, here are the recommendations to keep you safe:

» Arthritis—avoid strenuous exercise during any pain, flare-ups, or inflammation. It is safe to do gentle joint movements during these periods, but listen to how your body feels. Try to stretch during the times of day when the pain is the least severe or when pain medication may be at its most active time. Be cautious if you're taking anti-inflammatory medications (aspirin, ibuprofen, and naproxen sodium), as they can temporarily lessen your musculoskeletal pain and make it very easy to stretch and hurt yourself. If you find that your joints are hurting after a session, then you need to modify the stretch and the intensity you do it at for the next session. Be sure to be wearing shoes that can help with any shock absorption and stability. As you practice your stretches, it is highly recommended to focus on functional activities like standing up, step-ups, and stair climbing.

» Muscular Imbalance—when you have a muscular imbalance, you run the risk of creating a postural misalignment. Poor posture, weak and tight muscles, and repetitive movements can cause those muscular imbalances. For example, if you're a baseball pitcher and all you ever do is pitch, those muscles required to throw will be very strong, but the other muscles to do a different activity will be significantly weaker, which causes an imbalance. The imbalance can be a cause of serious injury if not corrected. While stretching, focus on the shorter muscle if the range of motion is compromised. If you sit at a desk all day, then your hips will most likely have a muscular imbalance. Try stretching more specifically with your lower back and legs to help those shorter muscles.

» Osteoporosis—if you want to practice flexibility, be cautious if you have osteopenia (low bone mass) or diagnosed osteoporosis. The goal for people that have osteoporosis is to avoid the risk of fractures. For safety measures, try to use a chair or handrail for support when they need it. When doing exercises, avoid those that would involve any bending, twisting, or compression on the spine, wrists, or hips. Specifically, people with osteoporosis should not do: bending forward (the forward fold pose), supine spinal rotation or twists, plow pose, and back extensions like the cobra pose.

» Hip Fracture or Replacement—now usually, if you're in this position, you will be assisted by a physical therapist to gain back your mobility, but if you want to continue on your own to help your range of motion, then note that you need to avoid exercises that involve excessive internal rotation of the hip (turning the foot inward), hip adduction (crossing the legs beyond the midline), and hip flexion (thigh more than parallel to the floor).

That's it! Now you know what I know about designing a flexibility program for yourself. Start out with the basics and decide your frequency, intensity, amount of time, the type of exercises, the volume (sixty seconds of flexibility exercise per joint is recommended), and the progression. Once you find those answers, then start plugging it into your weekly routine. It will make the difference, I promise. Happy stretching!

Chapter 14

SPECIAL POPULATIONS

"*I will praise thee; for I am fearfully and wonderfully made: marvelous are thy works; and that my soul knoweth right well*" (Psalm 139:14).

God has made every single one of us just as He had planned. Those of us that are young, those of us that are old, those of us with disabilities, and even those special mamas that are creating new life. I think you'll agree that no matter where we are in life, there's usually some circumstance that makes us believe we can't do what we wish we could. A lot of people, sadly, think they could never obtain a healthier lifestyle because they have diabetes, are seventy years old, are going through their third pregnancy with a tired body, have a physical disability, or whatever the situation may be. The truth of the matter is so far from it. God has actually designed our bodies to overcome physical situations even with difficult physical barriers.

I wanted to include a special populations chapter because I know God did not put this book on my heart for everyone, from far and few between. I'm writing this book for imperfect people that haven't been shown before that it is possible to improve their health even where they are at in life. So please, don't be discouraged and think you can never improve your situation. We know that "*...with God all things are possible*" (Matthew 19:26) and that God can work in your situation too.

I want you to know how important it is to address the lack of good health in certain populations like children, pregnant women, older individuals, and disabled. Of course, many outside situations tend to be the reason why these individuals can struggle with healthy living, but some just don't know how to exercise for their current state. I believe it is so important for all to know that even if they are in a challenging circumstance, if they don't know how, if they are scared or worried it could be hard, exercise can be easy and safe to learn. The benefits for special populations to exercise are so much more important and vital to good living that I encourage you that even if it seems like it may be hard or you're scared to try, just stick with me, and I think you'll see that it may be easier than you think. I think you'll see that anyone can be active, and anyone can experience a healthier lifestyle.

Children:

When it comes to kids, I'll be honest with you; activity is going to be one of the best fundamental things you can implement in their lives. I don't just mean that because I'm a lover of all things in health and fitness, but the studies show how vital it is for their growth. Several studies done by Healthline show that activity helps kids with strengthening bones and muscles, preventing excessive weight gain, reducing the risk of diabetes, cancer, and other conditions, improving children's mood by helping with depression, allowing children

214

to sleep more often and more fully. These are just the basic benefits that activity can do for children. Here's a really sad fact that breaks my heart, in 2017–2018, between the ages of two to seventeen years old, there were 14.4 million children affected by obesity in the United States. That's almost twenty percent of the younger population! That was only the statistics in 2017 and 2018. Just think of how much worse it has become ever since COVID-19 has happened.

Kids, now more than ever, are so inactive. A lot of children have no desire to play outside, learn new games, or practice motor skills. Instead, most kids are glued to a TV screen or a phone and spend less than thirty minutes a day being active. So what's the big deal? you may think. Childhood obesity isn't a new problem. You're right, it's not a new problem, but it's a big problem. Not only are we raising our children with poor health habits that can affect their mortality down the road, but we are not teaching them how to use their bodies that God designed.

Let me put it this way; I once watched a really interesting study about how much energy children burn in a day. A study took two NFL football players and told them they had to mimic the movements of two toddlers to test how active children are. For a whole day, these football players had to basically play a never-ending game of Simon Says. By mid-afternoon, those NFL players were absolutely dead. They had no energy left; they were exhausted and so badly wanted to rest. For a quick moment, the two toddlers sat on the grass quietly playing, and the football players were so grateful. However, their gratefulness only lasted about thirty seconds because the kids got back up to start running around. Oh, you should have heard the groans and complaints from the football players.

Funny as the study was to watch and relate to as we have been there with a child that never stops going, that's exactly the point I want you to think about. Children naturally have an abundance of energy. They always want to be doing something or going somewhere until they finally have depleted their energy storage and basically knock themselves out by being so tired. God has designed children to be active to constantly be learning and growing. He knew that for us to grow into adulthood, we would need quite a bit of energy to keep up with our curious minds about how far we can run, how high we can jump, how fast we can go. Children are constantly wanting to learn more, see more, do more. To do that, they have been created by God as little balls of energy so they can grow like He has designed. So now, when you think about the fact that children today are not wanting to go outside and play because their video game is more interesting, think also about the scary fact that those children aren't learning how high they can jump or how fast they can run. Those children aren't getting to experience how to use their imagination or tap into their creativity because it's all right in front of them. I want to encourage you today that it's time to take action in our children's lives and get them active again. It's time for them to go out and be those loveable little balls of energy that God perfectly designed.

Now when it comes to exercise, don't mistake me in thinking that I will tell you to make your child start lifting crazy weights or running long distances. There are some families that have children who do some impressive activities, but that's not required for every child. When it comes to children, the thing I will tell you to do is to get them active for at least sixty minutes a day. I'm sure you've probably heard or seen the commercials that are sponsored by the NFL to be active sixty minutes a day. It's honestly the truth. Science has found and proven that a healthy child is minimally active for sixty minutes. When we get to our cardio section, I will go into more detail about how to find ways to keep your child active for an hour. Here, however, I want to touch on using resistance training or bone loading in those sixty minutes as well.

Resistance Training:

So here's the quick and dirty now that we've taken a good while to talk about the reasons to let your child be active. When it comes to resistance training, it is actually good for your child to do simple weights. Now you don't have to drag your child to a gym to start curling weights, but you can introduce unstructured activity: playing on a playground, climbing trees, or games like tug of war. You can even structure their activity by having them lift small weights or using resistance bands. It may seem odd to suggest weight lifting for kids, but it is actually very beneficial for their bones and joints. If you want to go down the lifting road, use either their body weight or eight to fifteen repetitions of moderate fatigue for a child. Also, this should go without saying, but you must, must, must have your child perform good technique for any lifting to keep them from injury. If your child is going to start lifting, then you can organize that time to be included in their sixty minutes a day, at least three times a week.

Let's say you don't want to go the resistance training route (for most, it isn't quite a practical lifestyle), so then the next step is focusing on bone-loading activity. There's not one that is better for the other, but it all comes down to what your goal is for your child or your child's goal. When you introduce bone loading, think of entertaining activities like running, jumping rope, basketball, tennis, hopscotch, gymnastics, dancing, and soccer. Those are just a couple of suggestions for good activities, but you can Google several others that may fit your child's interest more. Again like resistance training, you can include bone loading in your sixty minutes a day and try to have them participate at least three times a week.

Cardio:

I can't tell you how much my heart reaches out for children to reach their full functional capacities. Perhaps it's because as a child, my parents were able to give me so many activities to do that really have advanced me as an adult. It may seem a little daunting at first to think about planning out your child's activity. But I think you'll find that once your child gets used to being active consistently, then nature will take its course. When it really comes down to it, any activity for any amount of time (obviously not pushing your child to do hours and hours past their ability) will be very beneficial for your child. Include it even in your own daily workouts! Have them start to learn what a push-up is, teach them how to do fast feet or how to jump rope with you. The point is, it's time to get your child active. Have them play active games like tag, relay races, hopscotch, agility training, and basically any activity that's going to get their heart pumping. It's super simple to find easy workouts for kids online that you can learn to implement in your daily life.

Pregnancy and Postpartum

This section is for all my pursuing to-be, expecting, and after pregnancy mamas. Unless you fellas have a wife you want to relay this to, you can skip this section. It's funny that when it comes to exercise that there's so much on the world wide web about what to do if you're expecting. However, the information that people put out there is good, but they tend to be poorly timed and sometimes miss the whole reason for sharing why they should be active. Actually, the main reason I believe that the information is well known is that yet again, another industry tries to make money off of moms that are looking for last-minute solutions or haven't had the resource to find answers on their own. There are suddenly these great packages for expecting moms of "bump boxes," protein shakes, exercise programs, and the like. Not that these products are bad at all, but they do thrive off the fact that they can make money. Oh sure, a gift package of a bump box can be a blessing for a mom that's been running in three different directions. But what about those moms that maybe can't afford those products? What about the moms that just want a simple "here's how to take care of yourself well while pregnant" type of information?

Well, that's exactly why I wanted to share this special section with you. God has designed women to have babies for hundreds and hundreds of years. Women were popping out babies before we had all of this new "stuff" that was supposedly going to make a night and day difference in your pregnancy. Now, I don't doubt that new discoveries certainly have been a blessing in keeping mamas and babies happier and healthier. There are, however, some fads out there that are just out there for profit, not truly looking into your wellbeing. That's what I want to show you. I want to lay out the proven facts of how you can take care of yourself with your own devices to keep you and your baby healthy. If you decide you want to invest in a bump box, then the more power to you.

This section is specifically for all moms, before and after birth. I hope that I can teach you the importance of exercise and the benefits of getting a good program started before you make that beautiful little miracle. I also want to encourage those that are already pregnant and help those mamas find a healthy schedule to stick to that will still be very beneficial. Lastly, I want to encourage my postpartum mamas that even though it may seem impossible to get back to where you started, it isn't. It will take dedication and patience, but I promise you your body will thank you when you're wanting to start trying for another child or if you're wanting to regain your body back that the time and effort are worth it.

It's amazing to think God has created women's bodies to perform the miracle of creating a little life and then designed the mother's body to return to its previous state. Now, of course, not everything goes back to normal, does it? Of course, we are blessed with stretch marks, body modifications, and the like. However, God's perfect design still allows us women to adapt to another strong, healthy body that can now be the active mother that your child needs. Let me tell you about an amazing example I heard of the other day.

There was this athletic lady that was trying to make the cut for the Olympics trails in a long-distance race. She is a phenomenal athlete that was dedicated to her sport and so focused on performing her very best. The husband and the athlete decided that it was time to start a family, even during her rigorous training. Soon you watched these videos of a four-month, six-month, eight, and even nine-month pregnant athlete running consistently and competitively daily. This mom-to-be was running several miles a day at incredible times. Finally, it was her due date, and she safely gave birth to a beautiful baby girl. One week after her labor, however, this amazing mom was progressing her body back into running shape. Within a couple of months, she was back in a fantastic running shape like she hadn't even had a baby. If this mom hadn't been training while she was pregnant, this would have been impossible. But as she trained through her pregnancy, her body made a much faster recovery. She soon after attempted her first Olympic trial and made it. I wasn't able to follow her much after that, but I do know she was one of the top twenty runners in the world. How incredible is it that someone who is carrying a full-term baby is still able to be so active? Some people think that really active moms are going to hurt their baby, but actually, the opposite is true. God created women's bodies to do incredible things, including being able to be active while being pregnant.

It's actually more a modern thing that women are not practicing an active lifestyle while being pregnant. In fact, it has now become more of a stereotype that moms get to take those nine months off.

That means it's free game for eating whatever and how much and even being inactive. Don't get me wrong, I am excited for the fact that I can justify some crazy cravings but just like everyday life, and what I've been saying all along is that you do need to balance some of those crazy habits. Now, I'm not saying that moms don't need to rest because, with all that is going on in your body, you do need to listen to what it needs. But what I'm trying to explain is that we've taken the idea of resting and made it into an ideal that pregnancy is just going to mess up our bodies no matter what. Even if you have the opportunity and ability to maintain your current level of health, what's the point?

Let me tell you how beneficial it is for pregnant women to take care of themselves well during pregnancy. When you eat well and stay active, you can prevent excessive weight gain, reduce the risk of gestational diabetes, lower the incidence of low back pain, and prevent excessive decreases in cardiorespiratory and muscular fitness. Did you catch the key word "excessive"? That's the point I'm trying to drive home. Yes, you can rest and take care of yourself as you create a life, but don't let that turn into an excessive amount of immobility that will cause you more issues down the road. Don't let yourself slide down the hill of excessive eating and cravings because it will be a hard journey to lose that weight afterward. It all comes down to balance like we've talked about all along.

Just think back to hundreds of years ago when women were caring for several children, making all their necessities by hand, and having to work around the house. They didn't have a choice but to be very active, but God designed us to be able to do such things even with a little one. You can still be active, eat well, and yet rest your body to keep yourself and your child safe.

Before Pregnancy

Now that we've covered some big items, let's dive into how we can actually obtain a healthier lifestyle. Let's first start with those who are not yet pregnant but are wanting to try. Now when it comes to the information of dos and don'ts of pregnancy, first and foremost, you need to have a good one-on-one with your doctor before you get pregnant about any possible concerns or situations you need to be aware of. Once you do become pregnant, then you need to have another conversation with your physician to see how they suggest you approach your pregnancy. Unless you have a complicated pregnancy, most doctors will tell you that you can participate in activities if you've been doing them before pregnancy. But also, you need to make sure that you have been participating in a program consistently, about three times a week for three months, to consider your activity regular. So if you're thinking of getting pregnant, I would suggest you take some time to make good healthy changes to your lifestyle and find a consistent routine before you start trying. I don't want to pop your bubble if you're wanting to try now. If that's the case, then I would suggest you find an easy exercise program to start at least three times a week, if not more. Then start to adjust to good eating habits as well. Try to be as dedicated as possible with your exercise and eating as you're trying. You may get pregnant right away, but if you've started an easy program, you can (if your doctor agrees) continue to pursue it as you go through pregnancy.

If you have been active before, you are going to start trying, then the same principles that apply to you that apply to the general population that is recommended by the US Surgeon General. You should shoot for at least thirty minutes of moderate-intensity physical activity on most but preferably every day of the week if you have an uncomplicated pregnancy. Also, if you are a recreational or competitive athlete, you can train safely during pregnancy at a higher volume and intensity if you are under close obstetric supervision.

Maybe you're wondering what exactly to do for exercise if you are not an athlete but just want to start a good program. Here's what is suggested.

Exercise mode: Walking and cycling can be one of the best forms, as it is easy to monitor exercise intensity. Any activity that increases your risk of falls, any abdominal trauma, and very rapid changes in your movement that can impact your balance are generally not recommended. Sports like skiing and skating, basketball and softball, tennis and volleyball, and especially activities at elevations are generally not recommended to pursue if you're pregnant because of the risk of an accident happening. It's not impossible for future moms to play these sports while pregnant, but more precautions need to be taken if you are going to participate in those activities, just like the pregnant Olympic volleyball player I mentioned. She could play but had to be very cautious.

Exercise intensity: When exercising, you should be aware of how much exertion you are putting in. For a woman that's pregnant, it is suggested that you stay somewhere between a light exertion and somewhat hard. Another way to evaluate your intensity is the talk test. Pregnant women should be able to hold a conversation while exercising. If you can't hold a conversation or it's difficult to talk, then you need to decrease the intensity.

Exercise session duration: When wondering how long you should exercise, you need to accumulate at least 150 minutes a week. That sounds like a long time, but if you can do 20 to 30 minutes every day, you'll find that hitting 150 minutes is easy. If you can't quite do 20 even, then break up your times throughout the day. In the morning, you can shoot for 10 to 15 minutes and then finish in the evening with another 10 to 15 minutes. If you feel like you have the energy to do more than 30 minutes, then you can pursue more time. Just be sure to pay attention to how your body is feeling.

Exercise frequency: I know before I mentioned that exercising every day is great if you're pregnant, which it is. However, if you are going to pursue an actual exercise program, then it is only recommended to do three to five days a week if you are hitting your goals of twenty to thirty minutes each time.

Flexibility: This seems like a simple one, but flexibility is something I cannot stress enough. Pregnancy and yoga go together like peanut butter and jelly; it's good together. We did talk a little about yoga, and the same applies for a yoga or flexibility program: every day for at least five to ten minutes. The only thing you need to be aware of is that you don't want to pursue an overly aggressive flexibility program, as, during pregnancy, you will have increased circulating levels of relaxin, and thus, it can cause potential ligament and joint capsule damage if not monitored well. Also, to state again, you need to avoid any supine poses, as it can become a potential obstruction of venous return and a risk of orthostatic hypotension.

So those are the recommendations for pregnant women who have been active before pregnancy. So as you are nearing that time, be sure to plan out a good, consistent, and obtainable program that you are confident will be the best approach to keep you active throughout your term. Unless you are, for example, an aspiring marathon runner, don't make yourself a really hard program to follow. Even if you've been pregnant before, so many things change when you become pregnant. The worst thing you could do is make something so difficult that you lose all aspiration to be active and slump back into inactivity, which is what we don't want. So the main idea: give yourself something you think is doable and easily obtainable.

Pregnant

If you are already pregnant and have not been participating in any activity before, then you need to go with what I call the daily twos. Yoga and walking are going to be your best friends during your pregnancy. Now you may not have been actively participating in yoga, but that's okay. Work your way slowly in a simple program. Start with a small amount of time, easy poses, and then slowly progress your way up as they get a little easier. If you're truly a beginner, then I would recommend starting with a ten (yes, only ten) minute program of simple exercises, and don't be discouraged if even ten minutes are hard. If that's the case, then start with five and build from there. Also, it's important to note during this time to listen to how your body feels. Even in yoga, there can be certain poses that don't feel good, so don't do them. Also, avoid poses that require you to lie supine on the ground if you are in your second trimester or close to twenty weeks. However, as you move through your pregnancy, yoga will be so beneficial for you to help reduce anxiety, relieve pain, keep your muscles activated, and keep you active.

When it comes to walking, it comes down to common sense. You walk as fast as you feel able and as long as you feel good. I would recommend that you walk every day for at least twenty to thirty minutes if you can. Again, if you don't feel like you can, then don't do it. Listen to what your body tells you. Are you exhausted after just fifteen minutes, or do you still have energy left? Decide what time fits best and progress as what feels best. Do you ache everywhere the next day after walking? Maybe take it down just a notch to let your body recover and do less amount of time the next day.

Just as I listed before in the "Before Pregnancy" section, those will be your recommendations for exercise and flexibility if you were active before you were pregnant. The main goal that you want to have during pregnancy is consistency. I don't want to give you false hope that if you exercise, your belly will be much flatter after giving birth. You will still have to put in some time to regain your body back to its normal, but it will be much easier and accomplished much sooner than if you were inactive your whole pregnancy. Trust me, the recovery time of an inactive pregnant mom compared to an active pregnant mom is not even comparable. It's worth the twenty to thirty minutes in your day for those nine months.

Sometimes fatigue, nausea, and vomiting may affect you in your first trimester, and that's okay. It is not recommended to push past those barriers to exercise. If you struggle with any of those symptoms, then the best thing you can do is exercise when you feel good and rest when you don't. A couple of things that you do need to be aware of are some signs and symptoms to be cautious of when exercising. If at any time you experience: vaginal bleeding, regular pain, amniotic fluid leakage, dyspnea prior to exertion, dizziness, muscle weakness affecting balance, calf pain or swelling, headache, and chest pain. These symptoms are no joke and can put you and your baby at risk. So if any of those pop up, then you need to terminate your exercise and speak to your doctor immediately. These situations are rare but still need to be cautious of.

The thing I want to bring your attention to is when you are exercising, you need to watch your calorie intake. As most of you moms probably already know, creating a baby takes a lot of energy. If you put exercise on top of that, you have to make sure you're replacing what you workout as well. Most pregnant women require at least 300 calories more a day just to fulfill their needs for pregnancy. So if you are going to exercise, then you need to calculate the estimated amount of calories you will burn in an exercise and then meet that same amount of burned calories as your intake.

Postpartum

Now when all the fun is over, and you've given birth to a beautiful baby, now is the time to start thinking of getting your body back into a healthy stage before the craziness of newborn life takes over, and you're fifty pounds overweight. I don't mean to make fun of moms that have gone through that situation. A new baby is no joke, and it will seem like you have no time, and the last thought moms can possibly think of is exercising. However, if you can start slowly while your baby is still young and not as active, it's easier in the long run to implement exercise when they're bigger and running around. Again, habits, while it may seem silly to think something so small, can make an impact and will be the key tool to getting you back in good shape. Also, don't forget starting a good and consistent eating regimen is the other key tool to get yourself into a healthy state. But we'll talk more about nutrition in our actual nutrition chapter.

So let's talk more about the moms that have a child and then wake up one day to find that they utterly despise their bodies and can't believe how much extra weight they've put on. Two things can happen here: one, the mom gets so motivated to lose the weight they become extremely dedicated to fitness that they do lose the weight and become even healthier than before they got pregnant (let's call those mom's "type a"); one is obviously ideal but rarely are moms able to make this happen. Type b, we'll say, is where the mom realizes what shape her body is in, hates the way she looks, but already admits defeat because change seems impossible. So right off the bat, type b thinks there is no way out and will just accept her "fate" as an overweight, unattractive mother. Here's what is so sad to me thinking of both types of these poor moms. The moms that are able to get themselves back in shape, our "type a," are usually motivated by earthly things like lust or jealousy. Those are strong words, I know, but remember back to our earlier chapters and how easily our minds go to those kinds of thoughts when we start comparing and contrasting our bodies with others. Those moms most likely saw pictures on social media or other fit moms and were so desirous of how they looked like and how badly they wanted to look like their old selves again they found an earthly motivation to get themselves back to their original state. Yes, they may have accomplished getting in shape, but it was for the wrong reasons. Remember if you're motivations to get fit are not God-honoring, then you will truly never find yourself happy with where you are at. That fit mom will constantly be trying to find some sort of justification for her body now that it's gone through pregnancy. She will be struggling with her body image every time she gets pregnant, and every time she gets back to fitness level, she believes it is where she wants to be.

Now let's also talk about the sad truth of those moms that give up trying to get back in shape. These types of mommas make my heart hurt for them because they are so unkind and unloving to the vessels that God made for them. Let's just remind ourselves that all of these moms just gave birth to a tiny, little human inside them. Of course, you won't look like yourself right away! But even after time, when they've neglected finding consistency and good habits, they still have a body that is serving another purpose, being a mother. But what is so sad for type b moms is that they develop this inward hatred for their body. What a shame! Just because you gained ten, twenty-five, fifty, or even a hundred pounds, your body is still beautiful! Yes, you may be out of shape, and your health could be in a dangerous area, but you are still God's creation and are still worth fighting for. Please don't give up the fight to keep your body healthy no matter where you are. It will be difficult, yes, but not impossible. We know, as I've quoted several times, that "...nothing is impossible with God" (Luke 1:37). You are beautiful, and you can do this. You can get your body back to a healthy state, but only if you give your negative, earthly thoughts to God. Instead, adopt positive and godly thoughts about your body. Give yourself goals that will honor and praise Him. Improve your body so that you can be an even better mother to your child. Improve your health so that when that little one is up and running around, you can too. Your fight is not over, and don't listen to this world that says it is. Instead, put up a fight and get back into the race for using your body as God's temple.

Now that we've had the motivational speech, let's talk brass tacks on how to actually succeed if you've just given birth. After you've had your baby, you will need to talk to your doctor when they suggest you start exercising. Most doctors recommend you can start exercising after six to eight weeks. If you had an easy pregnancy, then your doctor may tell you you can start earlier. However, if you had a complicated pregnancy or a C-section, you will most likely need to wait the eight weeks, if not longer, if prescribed by your doctor until you can pursue exercise. Don't get discouraged if you have to wait a little longer. Actually, the best thing you can do is to develop good eating habits during this time when you don't have to focus on exercise as well. That's actually my main piece of advice while you're waiting those six to eight weeks. While you're adjusting to your baby and adapting to eating enough to produce milk if you're breastfeeding, take this time to start to include a better holistic eating pattern. For more information on how to do this, refer to the nutritional chapter under pregnancy and postpartum.

When you are finally cleared to start exercising, here's what you need to know. Start light, progress slowly, eat well, and don't be discouraged. Let me explain what I mean:

Start Light—when you're picking up resistance training and cardio again, please don't go crazy and start working out as hard as you can. Obviously, your body will be quite tired and still recovering. But if you start working out that way and then when life happens, baby time gets crazy, the last thing you'll possibly want to do is exercise because you burned yourself out. So for creating good, long-lasting habits that can withstand even the craziness of a baby, start light. The only exception is that if you were working out consistently during your pregnancy, you can raise your intensity level but still keep it easy for the first couple of weeks.

Workout Recommendations: Resistance training—one to two times a week, full body. Cardio—two to three times a week, fifteen to thirty minutes max.

Progress Slow—just like we've talked about in the past of doing slow progressions to avoid burnout and a plateau, you need to progress even at a slower pace if you're recovering from birth. Not only is your body having to adapt to going back to normal, but you'll have all sorts of hormones to try and work around. Some days you'll feel like working out; other days will be less so. But if you can give yourself obtainable, long-term goals, it'll be easier for you to slowly progress and not be worried about getting those abs back as soon as possible but creating a lifestyle that'll stick.

Progression Recommendations: Normal recommendations are to progress one variable (time, intensity, weight, etc.) after four weeks. For postpartum, I suggest you take four to six weeks before you try to progress. It may take longer to feel adapted to your exercise, so take time to build that platform before making it harder. When you do increase a variable, do it in small increments. An example would be if you start off by doing fifteen minutes of cardio three times a week and are at the four to six-week mark, only progress to twenty minutes. If it's challenging but doable, stick to your guns. If it's too hard, stick with your fifteen minutes and give yourself another week or two and try again. Another note to you. Make sure you are progressing. Don't sit at an easy level unless you're satisfied with your current state of health. You won't be able to improve your health if you don't progress your exercise.

Eating Well—We'll touch more about nutrition for postpartum later, but I have some important keys for you to remember when thinking of exercise. If you start exercising after you've given birth but still continue to eat poorly, let me tell you that you will not see the results you want. I've said it before; when it comes to a healthy lifestyle, eating is 75 percent of your workout. Only 25 percent of your health actually revolves around your exercise. Eating well will affect your weight, your muscles, your hormonal balance, energy, and hon-

233

estly, the list continues on and on. The main mistake many mothers make after birth is that they keep eating the way they did before when they let themselves fall into their crazy cravings. Let me put it this way, if you're pregnant, need to consume at least 300 more calories a day, and you eat all the junk food, you will hit that 300 calorie goal and then some. Then you have your baby, and let's say you're going to breastfeed. If you are, then you'll luck out because most moms need to consume anywhere from 300–500 calories to fulfill their intake needs. However, we can still eat poorly and even over consume 300–500 calories easily if we've created the habit to just eat and eat while not watching how much. On the flip side, if you're not going to breastfeed, then there are 300–500 calories you don't need to intake, but many moms still do. So what's my point here? If you ate poorly during your pregnancy and continue to eat poorly after pregnancy, you will not lose the weight you want to lose. You won't see the benefits of your day-after-day workouts. This is the most common mistake for moms. So, if you can while pregnant, follow healthy eating habits. Once you've given birth, pick up those eating habits again. It may seem hard because you'll have some cravings, but trust me that eating in a balanced manner will actually help fulfill those cravings and needs better than eating junk food.

Don't be Discouraged—whatever you do or don't do, do not let the typical woman brain ruin all your plans and expectations of getting in shape. One of the worst things women have to struggle with when trying to get in better shape is their own brain. And I'm actually going to refer to "our brain" as a power that Satan uses to discourage us from having confidence in ourselves. I truly do mean that. There's this "resistance" that he puts up in our thoughts that make us think, *I will never lose this weight. All of my stretch marks are hideous. I'm a failure with exercise and eating. I'm so unattractive, and it'll never change.* Let me tell you, I struggle with those thoughts, and I'm not even pregnant. During and after pregnancy, those thoughts try to hit even harder. Heard of postpartum depression? Yeah, I honestly believe that's one of those things that Satan has used to his advantage to take away from the amazing miracle God created inside you. He tries to make you feel awful about yourself so that you won't have the joy to praise God for the miracle He made. Hear me now. I know it's hard, and I know those lies are very convincing, but they are not true. You were meant to have that baby, and you were designed to bring it perfectly into this world. But never, never believe that you can't do something or look a certain way because this world tries to tell you so. Do you think Mary struggled with how her body looked after she gave birth to Jesus and then gave her body to her husband, Joseph? I'm sure she did! Before Mary and Joseph even had the chance to enjoy each other, Mary already had gone through birth. I'm sure that the "woman's brain" kept trying to tell her lies about herself and her body. And she even gave birth to the Son of God! The point is that it will be hard; it will take time; you won't see the change you want right away. However, don't give up. Stick with it, and I promise you that just like in the story of the Hare and Tortoise, slow and steady wins the race.

Seniors

It's time to dive in and talk to those that are wiser than all of us youngsters. I'm talking about those who may have been blessed with those beautiful streaks of grey hair. Yes, I'm talking about our AARP members, our seniors. Now maybe you picked up this book and thought it would be more geared toward younger people. I'm sorry, younger people, but this book is actually geared for *everyone*. Whether you're a teenager, twenty to thirty years old, middle age, or a senior, my goal is to make this applicable for all ages and situations. Granted, there are certain situations I just can't address or have the knowledge to, but thankfully God gave me the knowledge to learn about health and fitness for a variety of ages, and yes, even seniors.

Now before you start thinking that I'm just a little know-it-all, I promise I'm not here just via my opinions to tell you what you should do. Yes, I do have my own opinions for sure, but I think for you to really succeed, you need to know the actual facts, not just what I think. I'm here with the schooling I was taught, facts that have been proven, and the tried and true methods that are so important for our seniors today. As a matter of fact, out of all the people I could teach about taking care of themselves, my passion tends to attract to teaching older individuals. I love sharing what I have learned in hopes that I can help improve their lifestyle to make every day a little better.

I think if there's one area that the fitness and health industry puts so little effort and care into, it's reaching out to our senior community to really help them improve their daily lives. Think about it, how often do you see some fitness ad posted on a gym or a TV commercial that shows a senior getting healthier when it's not some dopey-looking exercise machine or a magical diet? You don't see an ad for seniors that shows them actually using good pieces of equipment or getting out and exercising. What is usually displayed is a very bubbly-looking senior that is so happy with their little foot-pedal machine that is so convenient to do while they're sitting and watching TV. Now mind you, yes, some activity is better than none, but they're not encouraging seniors to be active; they're doing the exact opposite! Instead, the industry is trying to invent "convenient" machines that seniors can use without really having to do anything. Again, for some situations that some people can't get out of a chair by themselves, it can be a good idea. But for a majority that can still be active, it's doing a disservice because it won't help them improve their lifestyle; it'll only make them more inactive.

Now that I've had my ramble, let me tell you exactly what you need to know about activity that is so important for seniors. We've talked a little about the physiological changes with age but not a lot. Let me explain what exactly happens to our bodies as we age: from our hearts, brains, muscles, bones, blood flow, flexibility, heat and cold tolerance, balance, insulin sensitivity, and much more starts to decline as we age. I'm not saying this to scare you about old age. We will all age and all experience "slowing down." However, what I do what you to note that is yes, we start to decline as we age, but because so many seniors are inactive, they decline even faster, which can make daily life so difficult.

Here are some numbers for you to really see what I mean: In the average sedentary adult, they will decline in all areas of their body by 30 percent between the ages of thirty and seventy years old. Our muscle strength will decline starting at age thirty all through age eighty by 30 to 50 percent. That can be half our original strength we will lose. Females, we will steadily lose 1 percent of our bone density after thirty years of age steadily every year until after menopause; it then accelerates to 2 to 3 percent a year. Remember how most women struggle with osteoarthritis or osteoporosis? Bone density loss is a big reason why. Degeneration starts to hit the elastic components of connective tissue, which basically affects our mobility and stability in our joints. You become less flexible and easily can lose your balance.

So now here we are, thinking about all the ways we decline as we age. It's a little depressing, I'm sorry. But I told you from the beginning I was going to be blunt because it's information like this that most people don't know or don't know much of. This information is vital for all of us to know so that no matter where we are on the age scale, we realize the importance of how beneficial exercise and good eating habits can be for our lifelong health. So am I saying that exercise and eating right can help our looming decline? Why yes, yes it can.

Here's an encouraging percentage for you, only 50 percent of the previous degenerations listed are actually due to aging. So basically, no, there's not a "fountain of youth" exercise to keep you from getting older; it will still happen. However, the other 50 percent of those statistics are usually due to sedentary exercise and can be altered with exercise! Wow! Who would have thought that staying active can actually help you live better, longer, and happier! This information is so cool; maybe I should write a book about it…

When seniors get serious about exercising again, aerobic capacity and muscular strength can be increased by 20 to 30 percent. That's an incredible amount you could gain back! Literally, the 20 to 30 percent would mean the difference of being able to walk when you're in your seventies to nineties and not walking. Those percentages are even similar to what most young adults see when they exercise too. However, as previously mentioned, aerobic training can definitely improve exercise efficiency more in a senior than in a younger adult. Studies are showing that exercise does improve your quality of life and even your length of life. A large study was done on seniors that were sedentary compared to those who were mild to moderately active, and the thirty-eight studies found that those who were active reduced their all-cause mortality, whereas inactive seniors only increased their mortality. Have I convinced you yet? I promise you, the time spent to stay active will benefit you more than you could imagine. Do you want to take preventative measures to stay healthier so you can be out enjoying your family, or do you want to decline to such a poor state of health that you can't even get out of bed?

So now that you're hopefully motivated to start making some changes, the first thing you must do is go to your doctor. The chances are higher in an older adult of an underlying disease, so it's very important you talk with your doctor about what you can or can't do. Once your doctor gives you your stipulations, please stick to his or her orders. The chances of an incident are higher at your age, so be careful.

Now for seniors, cardiorespiratory fitness is arguably one of the most important goals in your exercise program. Even if your cardio is only a low-intensity level, it can still make a huge difference on premature mortality in middle age to older adults. Think of it this way, a 10 percent improvement in your cardiorespiratory fitness can produce a 15 percent decrease in your overall mortality. That's huge! When a trainer works with a senior for a couple of years and observes no chance, that's a great thing because that means there's no decline. That's what your goal needs to be as you start this journey for yourself. Find an achievable and realistic goal to be proactive about and work towards that.

So before you start your exercise program, first things first, you need to test yourself for where you are currently at. Can you walk up to five, ten, fifteen, twenty-five, or more minutes? If you can only do ten minutes of easy walking and be out of breath, then we need to start really light. If you're able to walk up to thirty minutes, then you can start at a little higher intensity. Let me tell you this: When it comes to seniors, we are not shooting for making you the fittest senior on the planet. Thus, that means that I'm not going to tell you that you need to do really high-intensity workouts. Unless you have some really impressive goals with your fitness, all you need to focus on for your intensity is a mild to moderate. So my favorite test is going to be the best way to measure your intensity, the talk test. While you're doing your exercise, if you can carry on a conversation easily, then you're going to be at a mild intensity. If you can talk but not consistently, I would say that's more of a moderate intensity. And finally, if you can't talk at all, that's vigorous, which I wouldn't suggest for you to shoot for unless, of course, you're trying to compete in the senior Olympics like my old track coach did.

So here's your instruction:

» Mild intensity—if you can only participate at a mild pace (which is completely fine and a great place to start), you need to be doing aerobic activities five to seven times a week for 15 minutes or more a day. Your goal should be to increase your time up to 30 minutes or more if you can. If you can hit a total goal of 100 to 150 minutes a week, you will be doing wonderful and can consider progressing towards a moderate pace if you can.

» Moderate intensity—if you can be active at a moderate pace, then you should shoot for being aerobically active five to six times a week for 30 minutes and even up to 60 for more benefits. Your goal should be to hit 150 to 300 minutes a week. It sounds daunting, I know, but this isn't you going out for a long run every day. These are easy aerobic activities to get you active again.

» Vigorous intensity—for those of you that have the health to train at this level, you only need to train three or more days a week at twenty to thirty minutes a day, coming down to seventy-five to a hundred minutes in a week.

Now that you know what intensity to shoot for, let me also tell you what aerobic activities you can do. It should also be known that any activity that will get you up and moving that you enjoy should already be on your list of exercises to pursue. For activities that are recommended for seniors: brisk walking, aquatic activities, stationary cycle, recumbent stepper, Zumba, and even Pilates. The nice thing about most of these activities, besides the aquatic activities, is that you can get set up to do this right in your home! Thanks to the creation of YouTube, you can actually just look up Zumba or Pilates lessons for seniors. You can invest in a stationary cycle and also browse online lessons for free. It's amazing that when we go to look, there are a lot of free and easy resources for living healthy. So what are you waiting for? Do some thinking on your end on what is realistic, practical, and maintainable for your aerobic activities and see if it can work for you.

When it comes to muscular strength, it is actually just as important for seniors to pursue resistance training because of the rapid muscle loss, like we discussed earlier. Once you get past the age of thirty, the saying "If you don't use it, you lose it" really comes to life. When we start to age, the muscle we've built up will start to slowly decrease if it's not used consistently. Muscle loss will result in issues with balance and mobility and can eventually create a problem with a lack of independence. Now obviously, I'm not going to suggest you start a bodybuilding program (however, some seniors have, and I must say I'm impressed), but I do want you to consider starting a resistance program. Again, before you start thinking it's not worth it, just consider this: muscle training in seniors has been proven to improve cognition, mood, self-confidence, self-esteem and obviously increase muscle mass that would help improve daily living. Staying active in resistance training can very well be the difference later down the road of you being able to get up out of your chair by yourself or having to be assisted every time. Which route would you rather pick?

Now that I hopefully have you convinced to pursue resistance training, there are a couple of items we need to discuss. First and foremost, whatever style of weight lifting you decide to pursue, you must have proper form. Not just for the benefit of doing it the right way but because your risk of injury will be so much higher, and recovery takes much longer now than it did when you were younger. Number two, it has been proven that actual free weight lifting (dumbbells, barbells, etc.) can be beneficial for seniors to use, but if you're not going to hire a personal trainer to show you the forms and spot you, it is safer to use resistance machines. If you're experienced in lifting weights, then by using your judgment, you can start using free weights. Most seniors, however, tend to be beginners when it comes to resistance training, so simple body weight, resistance bands, and machines tend to be the way to go.

Recommendations of Resistance Training Programs:

» *For Beginners:* One set of ten to fifteen repetitions is recommended for older adults unless they are more advanced lifters. Make sure and pick a weight that you can do ten to fifteen repetitions of. Pick eight to ten that will include the major muscle groups. This is a must for your resistance program. You want to make sure you are working all the different yet very important muscles.

» *Major Muscle Groups:* Biceps, triceps, deltoids, chest, erector spinae, gastrocnemius and soleus, gluteus maximus, hamstrings, quadriceps, trapezius, latissimus dorsi and rhomboids, obliques. To make it a little easier to remember, just think of these muscle groups: arms, shoulders, chest, back, hips, and legs. The effort you put in for your exercises should be light for beginners and progress up to moderate and even vigorous.

» *Exercise Duration:* All you need to do is to complete one set of your eight to ten exercises. And make sure in between all exercises you allow adequate rest, one to two minutes in between.

» *Frequency*: pursue two or more days a week of resistance training.

Now maybe you're thinking, *It really can't be that simple to design a program, can it?* Cool news, it actually can. Most people don't like designing their own programs just because they simply don't know how to. However, once you're given the specific numbers and given a direction to go, it's quite easy to piece together. So as you're deciding to pick up your resistance training, you can either make the decision to go try some machines or even free weights at the gym. Or, if you would feel more comfortable in your own home, I would highly suggest two things, YouTube and resistance bands. Do a quick search on the internet (if you don't know how then see if you can ask a handy grandkid if they're close) and search up light resistance bands. Choose a small variety that varies in weight. Secondly, use YouTube again and search body weight programs for seniors. You'll be amazed how many people have made videos for that category. Once you're there, give yourself a grace period where you try different exercises to see if it's too easy or hard. You may have to play around a bit to find what works for you or even modify it to work. Stick to your guns and stick it out. I promise that if you stick to resistance training, you will see a difference in your body. Suddenly standing up and sitting down can be easier. Back pain can be lessened, and your balance can improve.

The last thing I want you to include in your exercise program is flexibility. As we age, our range of motion is compromised. On average, we can lose up to 57 percent of our flexibility merely by age sixty-five. Limited flexibility associated with poor musculoskeletal strength can cause a large decrease in the abilities to do daily activities. So a lot of scientific studies have been done to see how beneficial stretching is for adults, especially seniors. The results are phenomenal, showing that it helps joint mobility, helps reduce deterioration of joints, can help with pain, and helps with balance. Balance, on another note, will be huge to retaining your ability of everyday living. Flexibility and strength training will be the best route to take to keep your balance steady.

When it comes to your flexibility, it's quite simple. Older adults should try to gently increase the amount they can stretch beyond their typical everyday activities at least two times a week, if not more. So basically, I'm saying that if you can stand and reach down and pick something off the ground, your stretch needs to be reaching up to or past your toes to stretch it past your normal. Now keep in mind when stretching, the direction is to stretch up until you feel a slight discomfort in your muscle. Don't ever push yourself past the slight discomfort in regards to causing injury. Progress each week as the stretches get easier, and push yourself a little further. The guidelines for stretching are simply these: hold a stretch for thirty seconds and repeat a total of three times. If you can't hold for thirty seconds, then start your way from five, ten, twenty-five, and then thirty. Progress with what feels good for your joints. Doing yoga will be the same idea and can also help strengthen muscles simultaneously. Consider YouTubing a senior yoga flexibility program two to three times a week. I guarantee, within a month, you will be feeling the difference.

The current guidelines for your frequency, duration, and balance exercises and balance training should happen at least three days a week for ten to fifteen minutes. You can easily include your balance training in your resistance training days. Again, a good yoga program could also be focused on your flexibility and balance. If you struggle with balance today, then don't worry. With time and persistence, you can gain back those muscles that will keep you healthy and safe. Start slow with easy exercises and short times and slowly progress yourself until you're at the point you want to be. After that, you need to continue your exercises to maintain what you have built.

That's all I have for you on the subject of senior training. It is so vital that you start taking an interest in your overall health as you are growing older. We all need to exercise, but it's even more vital for those who are older to maintain a healthy lifestyle.

Chapter 15

DESIGNING YOUR PROGRAM

We always thank God, the Father of our Lord Jesus Christ, when we pray for you, because we have heard of your faith in Christ Jesus and of the love you have for all God's people—the faith and love that spring from the hope stored up for you in heaven and about which you have already heard in the true message of the gospel that has come to you. In the same way, the gospel is bearing fruit and growing throughout the whole world—just as it has been doing among you since the day you heard it and truly understood God's grace...For this reason, since the day we heard about you, we have not stopped praying for you. We continually ask God to fill you with the knowledge of his will through all the wisdom and understanding that the Spirit gives, so that you may live a life worth of the Lord and please him in every way: bearing fruit in every good work, growing in the knowledge of God, being strengthened with all power according to his glorious might so that you may have great endurance and patience, and giving joyful thanks to the Father, who has qualified you to share in the inheritance of his holy people in the kingdom of light.

1 Colossians 1:3–6, 9–12

We read in this passage that the apostle Paul is greeting the Colossian Christians, for which he shows gratitude for their faith. Paul then moves on to talk about a prayer he has for those Christians that they may continue to grow and serve Christ. I think there's an important lesson to be learned here from Paul. You can genuinely feel his love for these people. There's a strong feeling of heart that wants them to succeed in this life, and that's how I believe God wants all of his children to love one another.

We live in a world today that does not focus on encouragement, love, support, or forgiveness. This world instead focuses on lustily, selfish things. This is not new, nor is it a surprise to God. I'm so thankful, however, that in the Word, there are such encouraging examples to follow, like Paul, when it comes to lifting others up.

I want you to reread verses 10 and 11. I want you to notice how Paul is telling the Colossians that he will pray for them to be filled with knowledge, wisdom, and understanding from the Spirit so that they can serve the Lord and please Him. Through their service, he prays that they will bear fruit in their good works, continue to grow in their knowledge of God, and be strengthened by the Lord so they can endure this world. I don't know about you, but that's a pretty powerful prayer. I think we all need someone like Paul to pray that kind of prayer for us as we face this world. This is actually what my heart wants to say to you today. I want to encourage you to have a healthy life so that you can bear fruits in your good works. I want you to be healthy so that you can continue to grow in your knowledge and faith in the Lord. I so badly want a healthier you to be strengthened by His power so that you can have the endurance and patience needed to go out and share the light He's put inside you.

When you sit down to design your program, whatever your goals and aspirations may be, I want you to be encouraged like the Colossians must have been by Paul. I want you to succeed in being able to serve the Lord, and that's why I've wanted to give you the tools to do so. Design your program to make you prosperous in this life as a Christian, not as the world desires you to prosper.

Comprehensive Exercise Program

You already know the majority of the tools you need to design your program. This chapter is simply going to give you the outline you need so that you can plug in all of the pieces together. Here's the meat and potatoes from ACSM:

» *Warm-up:* at least five to ten minutes of low- to moderate-intensity cardiorespiratory and muscular endurance activities.

» *Conditioning:* at least twenty to sixty minutes of aerobic, resistance, neuromotor, and/or sports activities (exercise bouts of ten minutes are acceptable if the individual accumulates at least twenty to sixty minutes a day of daily aerobic exercise).

» *Cooldown*: at least five to ten minutes of low- to moderate-intensity cardiorespiratory and muscular endurance activities.

» *Flexibility*: at least ten minutes of stretching exercises performed after the warm-up or cooldown phase.

So take this basic layout for a program, write it down, and start plugging in the cardio that you enjoy, the type of resistance training you'll pursue, and plan out the flexibility. It's not enough to just think of a couple of things and try to plug it in when you have time. That route doesn't work, I promise. Remember how we've talked about how habits are key? When you simply just have some exercises planned out for a free day, you'll never create a true habit that can stick. When your plans are wishy-washy, so will your workouts. Instead, have a month-to-month plan. It has been studied and researched that the most successful exercise programs are the ones planned out in advance and have structure. So don't skip this step; take the extra ten to twenty minutes to really plan out this program for your benefit.

The next couple of sections will maintain the overviews of the FITT principles for each aspect of your training. Get your list ready to plan out that routine!

Cardiorespiratory

Frequency: Remember some activity is better than nothing at all. So even if you have to start with the most simple of activities a week, start there. For general recommendations: three to five days a week. When you're deciding your frequency, also remember what intensity you'll use in conjunction as well. As you progress and increase your intensity level, your days recommended a week will decrease. So if you start at five days of moderate-intensity workouts and then progress to vigorous, lower your workout days to three or maybe four.

Intensity: As I've said before, you can do the talk test to find the exact intensity you should start at. As not everyone desires to go the exact route, I always suggest people to try the talk test first. For those that are sedentary and very deconditioned, the suggested intensity is very low (30 percent to 39 percent of your max intensity), but as you progress, that percentage or effort you put in can increase. If you have a high activity level, it's usually suggested to shoot for a moderate-vigorous intensity (60 percent to 89 percent).

Time: This merely means the amount of time you spend physically working out. General recommendations are based on your intensity. However, if you want to make a more flexible plan or have special circumstances, then look into the "Special Populations" chapter for more information.

Moderate-intensity: 30 minutes a day for at least five days a week for a total of at least 150 minutes per week, or you can break it up in different ways. You could do more than 30 minutes to do fewer days a week or do less than 30 minutes but would have more days a week of exercise. Whichever you would enjoy better is the best!

Vigorous-Intensity: Twenty to twenty-five minutes per day or a least three days a week for a total of seventy-five minutes. Same thing here as moderate intensity. Just try to hit the total amount of minutes in your week. If you want to split up your numbers differently on your days, then do whatever is best.

Combination: do both moderate and vigorous exercises for a twenty- to thirty-minute bout for at least three to four days per week.

Type: The type of workout is basically your mode. So for a cardio example, that could be walking, jogging, running, cycling, swimming, aerobic-based machines, jump rope, HITT, etc. Remember to pick an activity that will match your current activity level.

Volume: The volume is basically the overall energy expenditure you will produce during your workout. This comes down to your Metabolic Equivalents (METS). *"Neuromotor-enhancing activities focus on the communication between feedback from the periphery (e.g., arms and legs) and the interpretation by the central nervous system (e.g., brain and spinal cord)"* (Battista 2018).

Progression: This all depends on your health status, how fast you respond to your training, your fitness, and your personal goals. The goal of progression is to prevent stagnation in your training. Usually, only one variable is changed, whether that is intensity, time, or type. Time or the minutes per session is the recommended variable to progress. After about one month of frequent exercising, the frequency, time, and intensity should be gradually increased over the next four to eight months. This may be altered for individuals that are very deconditioned.

Muscular Fitness

This applies both to muscular strength and endurance. Strength is the ability of a muscle or muscle group to exert force, whereas endurance is the ability of a muscle or muscle group to continue to perform without fatigue. So the following FITT Principles will be focusing on exposing muscles to an overload, which is a stress beyond the typical amount that muscle performs. Over time, your muscles will adapt to the resistance to which you have to also progress to continue to build the muscle.

Frequency: As said before, there is both muscular strength and endurance to focus on. So all of the FITT principles will depend on which your goals are. Do you want to build muscle? Then you should be focusing on strength training. If you want to build up endurance, then that's the training you should focus on. For general recommendations for resistance training, you should be working the major muscle groups (chest, shoulders, back, abdomen, hips, and legs) at least two to three days a week. You also should note that it is imperative that you allow a forty-eight-hour window of recovery time for muscles worked. So if you worked out your chest and triceps on Monday, wait until Wednesday at least to work them again. Proper rest and recovery will allow you to be much more successful in keeping yourself safe from injury, with greater muscle gains and less chance of burnout. You can focus on doing separate muscle groups on certain days or do whole-body workouts for all muscle groups on one day. Depending on how you want to schedule your routine, still make sure you are targeting those muscle groups two to three times a week.

Frequency: Depends on what stage you are at in your lifting ability. Refer to the sample workout program to see recommended frequency on your level.

Intensity: This is connected to the number of repetitions you are shooting for. The heavier the weight, the lower your number of repetitions. If you're doing a lighter weight, then the higher your repetitions will be. The general recommendation is eight to twelve reps to improve overall muscular fitness. If you want to be really specific, then you need to work at a sixty to eighty percent level of your one rep max. For older populations and deconditioned persons, you can work at a lower intensity, forty to fifty percent of your one rep max to start. It is suggested to do the number of repetitions that allow your muscles to feel fatigued at the end of a set but not result in failure to do a set to make sure you are taking good precautions from injury and proper work of a muscle.

Time (duration): Again, this variable will depend on what your goal is for RT. When comparing split-body training and whole-body training, there will be a difference of time spent on each exercise and the total duration. The general recommendation for adults is that each muscle group needs to be trained with two to four sets with a rest interval of two to three minutes in between your sets. Of course, more sets like four compared to two sets will be more effective, but for those of you just starting out, you need to remember that even just one single set will improve your muscular strength. When deciding the number of your sets, pay close attention to the adherence to the schedule, as you'll want to organize it in a way you're sure to stick to. If you don't like a certain workout type of schedule, then change it!

Type (mode): There are several different types of RT, free weights, machines, rubber bands/cords, and body weight. There's no "perfect" RT style; it just depends on what you like and what is applicable to your goals. When putting the program together, you do need to focus on including multi-joint exercises (bench press, leg press, or something that will include multiple joints at one time) and single-joint (biceps curl, quadriceps extensions, or something only using one joint). Also, be sure to include opposing muscle group exercises (agonists and antagonists) in order to prevent muscle imbalances.

Volume: The minimum muscle groups that should be trained are two to four sets. They can be the same exercise or a combination of exercises that will affect the same muscle group. For example, if you did two sets of push-ups that target the chest and triceps, you could also do two sets of chest press machine to work the same muscles.

Progression: There are many ways that people like to progress when it comes to RT. The main thing I want to remind you of is that when you progress, make sure you progress all major muscle groups, not just the ones you're thriving in. Have you ever heard of the jokes about the big guys that have huge upper bodies but little chicken legs? The reason there's a stereotype about it is that some people get so motivated for the areas they like that they will always focus on building them but will forget or not pay attention to other areas. Again, remember us talking about muscle imbalances? The same is true when progressing. Make sure you're progressing even those areas that are a little harder to work on to make sure every area is happy and balanced. When it comes down to your actual progression, it again depends on your goals. If you reach a point where you are as strong as you want to be, all you need to focus on is maintaining it. You can't stop working out once you reach your desired level; otherwise, you will lose all of your hard work. To maintain muscular strength, you only need to train those muscle groups as little as one day per week as long as you're training at the intensity or resistance that they built up to. As for continuing to build strength or endurance, the amount of weight you lift and/or the amount of reps will be the progression you can use. You can also build up to more difficult exercises that challenge your muscles in a different way.

Sample resistance training program from ACSM's Resources for the Personal Trainer:

Beginner: this will take about two to three months remaining at this level until you feel comfortable to advance.

» Exercise: You should shoot for a total of six exercises. Select an exercise from one of the following: hips and legs, chest, back, shoulders, low back, and abdominals.

» Number of sets: One to three. Even just one set will be very beneficial for you if you're working on starting a routine. As you progress, you can include more sets.

» Number of reps: The beginner amount can be three to six reps but not to failure. You want to just start challenging your muscles, not killing them.

» Frequency: Two to three days a week. Even if you're doing light resistance training, you need more than one day to really hit all target muscle groups.

Intermediate: this level takes about three to twelve months to grow from, but it depends on your consistency as well as your current level going into this program.

» Exercise: You need to shoot for a total of ten exercises. Don't let that number scare you; it doesn't have to be a big lift. This is so you can include most muscle groups easily in your workouts. You need to work out these areas: hips and legs, quadriceps, hamstrings, chest, back, shoulders, biceps, triceps, low back, and abdominals. You'll notice that the more advanced you are, the more specific muscles you will be suggested to work. At this stage, you should be working about three to four days a week.

» Number of sets: One to three sets. Just like beginners, you want to start in a good range for your current fitness. Pick whichever challenges you but still will allow you to perform the exercises with good form.

» Number of reps: Depending on your level, you can choose ten to fifteen reps or eight to twelve. This depends on your goals. If you're strong enough to pursue heavier weights, then I would suggest eight to twelve. If you're still building your bass muscle, then go with ten to fifteen.

» Frequency: three to four days a week.

Advanced: Usually, advanced lifters have different goals and will have to spend longer time periods in muscular fitness areas that will be an expanded and extended training program. The more muscle you are working on, the more time you need to spend on it, as well as it could take longer to see specific results or shorter depending on the time dedicated.

» Exercise: Most advanced lifters will do anywhere from six to ten exercises on their lift days. Again, this is dependent on their goals. If someone is working their upper body, there are easily ten exercises they can choose to challenge themselves. However, if they're more specific, like chest and biceps, they may only need six to eight to really hit those muscles well. Advanced lifters need to pick exercises that will accomplish their specific goals for different muscles groups.

» Number of sets: for advanced, the suggested amount is three to six sets per exercise.

» Number of reps: only one to six reps depending on what the weight is.

» Frequency: four to five days a week.

Flexibility

Remember this area is to focus on improving your range of motion.

Frequency: Whatever style of stretching you choose, focus on two to three days each week for adults. More daily flexibility is most effective as well.

Intensity: This intensity is a little different than the other modes of exercise. When stretching, you want to stretch to a point of slight tightness, and you don't want to move too far past that to prevent hypermobility. If you're stretching and get to a point of discomfort, you need to release the stretch and not push as far. A stretch should never be painful.

Time (duration): general recommendations are ten minutes per session to allow all major muscle-tendon groups to be targeted with at least a minimum of four reps of each stretch.

Type (mode): You can use a very wide variety of stretches that we've discussed previously, static, active and passive, dynamic or slow movement, PNF, or even ballistic stretching. All can be beneficial for flexibility, depending on your goals.

Volume: Each stretch should be held at the point of tightness for ten to thirty seconds, repeated two to six times to result in sixty seconds total for the stretch. For PNF stretching, you should hold at a 20 percent to 75 percent maximum voluntary contraction for three to six seconds, then follow with ten to thirty seconds of assisted stretching. You should perform the flexibility exercises at least two to three days per week.

Progression: As you get more flexible, line it up with your goals. If your goal is to be able to touch your toes, slowly work towards that until you achieve it. Once you do, make sure you are still practicing the same exercises so you can keep the flexibility. If you want to further your flexibility, you will need to continue to challenge yourself in your stretches.

Neuromotor Exercise

The last thing we need to talk about is Neuromotor Exercise (NE). This type of exercise is one we haven't discussed very much because most people tend to include activities unknowingly. However, some people also may not realize that they leave these NE out of their programs. Neuromotor Exercise involves balance, coordination, agility, and proprioceptive training. Technically this training is considered functional fitness or movement. *"Neuromotor-enhancing activities focus on the communication between feedback from the periphery (e.g., arms and legs) and the interpretation by the central nervous system (e.g., brain and spinal cord)"* (Battista 2018). Any type of training with an overload will create improvements. This type of training is particularly important for those who are older and are at a higher risk for falls.

Frequency: It is recommended to exercise in this activity at least two to three days a week for at least twenty to thirty minutes for older adults. For younger persons, you can incorporate it in your daily activity exercises unless focusing on physical therapy.

Intensity: There are three ways in which the intensity can be manipulated: (1) base of support (narrowing the base will increase the challenge), (2) center of mass (displacement of the center of mass will increase the challenge), and (3) peripheral cues (visual, vestibular, and proprioceptive pathways).

Time (duration): As said previously, general recommendations are twenty to thirty minutes a day, or you can do more for a total of sixty minutes a week. If you prefer the tai chi route, you can incorporate your NE exercise and do forty-five to sixty minutes a day.

Type (mode): you can pursue tai chi, yoga, and Pilates for different types.

Advanced Training

As you progress in your training, or if you're starting out at a more advanced level, then you can increase your challenge in the FITT principles. You also can challenge yourself by adding or replacing older exercises with new ones that focus on different components of skill. I personally like to suggest to people that once you've done a program for three to six months, try to find similar exercises that still work the muscles you are focusing on, but find a different type of movement to target muscles in a different way.

You also can focus on trying different types of training like hypertrophy, endurance, strength, and power. These types of training work the muscles in different ways and are good to make you very versatile. Other than the components mentioned in this chapter, this is the simple way to design your program. It may seem like a little bit of work to plan it out, but I promise in the long run, it will benefit you more if you have a precise schedule to stick to. The more you can create habits, routines, and the like, the better your chances of creating a behavior modification that will last a lifetime.

Chapter 16

THE TRUTH OF GOOD EXERCISE

No one lights a lamp and puts it in a place where it will be hidden, or under a bowl. Instead they put it on its stand, so that those who come in may see the light. Your eye is the lamp of your body. When your eyes are healthy, your whole body also is full of light. But when they are unhealthy, your body also is full of darkness. See to it, then, that the light within you is not darkness. Therefore, if your whole body is full of light, and no part of it dark, it will be just as full of light as when a lamp shines its light on you.

Luke 11:33–36

In chapter 11 of Luke, Jesus is teaching and warning a crowd of things of this world. Verses 33–36 is a very clear warning of Jesus of hypocrites that refused to see the light of Jesus's life. He gives us an example of those who do not wish to see will become spiritually blind; they become miserable and full of darkness (sin). However, when we let our eyes focus on God, then our bodies are filled with His light, and we can shine for others to see.

I absolutely love this passage in Luke. Jesus is speaking to us on such a personal level because He knows what we are challenged in our lives, but He also shows us the way to win over those challenges. Moreover, as life has continued on since Jesus stated this important lesson, more and more hypocrites have surfaced today to try and convince us in any aspect of our lives to not follow after Jesus. We see this commonly in situations where a young teenager struggles whether or not to listen to his or her peers, coworkers, or friends try to convince you of habits that "are not that bad"; people can tease you for being "too Christian" or a "goody two-shoes."

I personally remember several taunts from high school. I'm so grateful for good parents who taught me strong morals and showed me how to have a relationship with Christ. So in my last middle school year, my parents decided to have my sister go part-time to public school. We had been taught all our lives at home, but it was time to start to learn the public education system. That first year was quite a shock, as I was unused to unruly peers and little influence of Christ in school. High school was even worse, as I started to make more friends, become a little more popular due to sports, and learn how the world really works. I remember trying to just do my best in school, respect my teachers, and be courteous. However, I also remember being teased for being a "goody two-shoes" and the like. This never bothered me because I knew that being a good kid was far more important and valuable than risking it all for something dumb. Even then, however, my peers tried and tried to get me to go down roads that were not Christ-like. They were, if you will, the influences that were trying to blind my spiritual eyes. Now, I won't pretend I never fell prey to those temptations because I did. But thankfully, I always had my parents to correct me on a better path and an always forgiving Father. My point in all of this is that this world will continue to try to blind us with temptations and immoral ways until Jesus comes back.

I think Jesus was suggesting to the idea that in any way in this life, we will be tried by hypocrites to somehow blind our spiritual eyes. These people may try with the way we talk, what we listen to, how we use our bodies, what our actions are or not, and yes, I believe that even the way we treat our bodies. Ah yes, here's the point you've been waiting for. This world has several avenues to try and trick us up, but one avenue very rarely discussed is what we do with our bodies. I'm not just talking about adultery and things like that, even though that is a very prominent issue today. I'm talking about what we believe is true about our bodies and the things we'll do to it to see something change.

This isn't a new subject, as I've talked about this idea in previous chapters. What I haven't discussed with you in depth, however, are the real truths of health, the false things about health, and how to avoid them. As we dive into this subject, I hope this opens your eyes to different ways that maybe you've been tempted to go down a road that blinds your eyes, a road that could make your whole body unhealthy.

Habits Are Key

We've talked before about how habits are so vital to creating lifelong behavior modifications. It takes three months, thirty minutes at least three days a week, of exercise to create an actual habit. But once you've created a habit, how do you keep from falling down other loopholes and relapsing in your progress? Well, the first answer is that you have to accept that you will have bad days, weeks, months, or even yes, years. You will not be able to keep a perfect program because life will eventually get in the way. My pastor has a wonderful saying, "If you're not currently in a storm, then you're either coming out of one or about to go into one." This is probably one of the best ways I've ever heard life described by. God is constantly refining us, and there's always going to be sin in the world until He comes home; thus, our lives will always be ever-changing. However, when we fall down, we don't have to guilt-trip ourselves or beat ourselves up when we fail.

I can't tell you how many times I'll have a fun "weekend" with little activity and junk food. I'll immediately feel bad and start to have such horrible thoughts about myself. Other times I've worked out for months upon months, and then one change will uproot my schedule completely, and I'll stop working out for a whole month and pretty much lose all my progress. That's when I really hear those bad thoughts swim around in my head. First and foremost, let's agree that those "thoughts" are really just Satan trying to make us feel less about ourselves. Remember God has made us just how He intended, and we have to push those awful thoughts aside so we can instead focus on His joy. When I have a storm pop up in my life, there are times when the thinking of my poor habits will consume me and make me a very miserable person. It's times like that that I have to turn over those thoughts to God and let Him guide me forward.

266

You are never too far gone, and you'll never be perfect either, so once you're able to realize that there will be times that you will be successful and times that you will fall, the better you will prepare yourself as you design your new life habits. That being said, it's also important to note that this world will continue to try and convince you that you can get anything instantaneously. Dr. Oz will always advertise the newest and greatest magical fruit that's supposed to make you drop pounds like nothing. There will always be the new, up-and-coming personal trainer that will have "suddenly" found the key to quick weight loss. I promise you this, the science in the area of health and fitness doesn't lie. Those who claim this or that don't have the science to back them up. If you want to know how to spot a "fake" health and fitness fad, then Google the advertisement, look up whatever articles they include, and see if they're good content. The articles are great if they have renowned doctors and study centers that published their research. The content is based well if it has the stamp of approval from legitimate fitness industries like ACSM and NASM. Basically, if the "research" is based on some unknown doctor or research place is unheard of, it's more than likely a facade.

So while you're starting on your journey, remember that your habits will be the key in creating a healthier lifestyle, not all of these fads that keep popping up. There's a reason why fads don't stick around but fade over time. So trust in the science of how the body works and how it needs to work to see results and be consistent.

Results Take Time, and Here's Why

This is another concept we've talked about in previous chapters, but it's something worth saying a couple of times because not everyone really believes it the first time around. As mentioned in the habits portion, these fads today pop in and out to make us believe that we really can get our dream bodies in a short period of time. Let me remind you if you didn't have a job, a family, lots of money, unlimited resources for nutrition, and endless motivation, you probably could get the results in a very short amount of time. However, who's to say that once you get there, you'll have any motivation to continue the extremely hard lifestyle you've started? That's how these gimmicks work. They expect you to have limitless time and resources to make all of it happen. We never do, do we?

For the average adult with the added-on situations of life, the results you want to get will take time, I promise. I don't say that to deflate you but to make you aware of how things work. We live in an age where everyone wants everything instantly. Kids want the new iPhone even though their old phone works just fine. A new car or truck comes out, and everyone rushes to go get it. We wish this person would communicate faster or that person would give us that promotion already. It's the age where time is money, and for the fitness industry, the more they can make everyone believe it's possible to get what you want faster, the more money they will make.

If we get into the science of it all, the body is very complex and isn't a machine. You have a lot of inner workings that are always functioning that result in the outcome of your health. This concept is basically summed up to exercise physiology. Exercise physiology is the study of how the body systems react to the "stress" of exercise. Those systems involved are the cardiovascular, respiratory, muscular, skeletal, and nervous systems. Let's do a quick breakdown of those systems to see what actually happens to them when you start to exercise.

Cardiovascular System: Your cardio system involves the heart and the blood vessels. God designed this system so that the cardiovascular system would deliver nutrients to and remove metabolic waste products from your tissues. More specifically, your cardiovascular system transports deoxygenated blood from the heart to the lungs and then takes oxygenated blood from the lungs to the heart. Your CV (cardiovascular system) also transports that oxygenated and deoxygenated blood back and forth from your heart to your tissues. The specific nutrients your CV moves are things like glucose (which is used for energy), free fatty acids (they are energy sources and membrane constituents), and amino acids (which are the building blocks for protein) to the cells. Very important for us to function properly. The CV then helps with the removal of your metabolic wastes like carbon dioxide, urea, lactate, etc., to which it is eliminated or rescued. Lastly, your CV helps with the regulation of your pH levels, transportation of hormones and enzymes for physiological function, maintenance of fluid balance to prevent dehydration, and lastly, maintenance of body temperature.

As you can see, your CV does a lot for you, and when you start to eat healthier foods and start to be active, all of these functions start to adjust to a new energy source and stress that's put on it. It doesn't happen overnight that your heart starts to work more efficiently when you start exercising and eating better; it takes several consistent months for that to take place. Even that change will be small, however! It will get better and better over time as you continue to be active and eat healthily.

Also, consider other changes that can happen to the heart the more you change your lifestyle: better blood flow, healthier heart rate, improved blood pressure, and more oxygen consumption. So many things are affected by our lifestyle! All the more important for us to adopt a healthy one.

The next one to overview is our *Respiratory System* (RS). The RS helps filter the air that comes into your body and allows gas exchange to take place in the alveoli. Alveoli are microscopic air sacs in your lungs. Basically, the air you breathe in will be filtered by these cool little dudes in your lungs. If you've ever started running when you haven't for a long time or suddenly try being active at a higher altitude than you're used to, you'll notice that it's much harder to breathe. Sometimes it makes us feel ill, and we have to stop our activity. There are several "sciency" things that happen, but chiefly our lungs are not used to that type of *active breathing*. Active breathing is when our ventilatory requirements are increased from our normal passive breathing. So when you start to exercise, all sorts of different muscles are suddenly put to use to help you open up for more air; however, if you haven't used those muscles for some time, then it's going to be a bit of a shock to your system.

Your lungs also help with the distribution of your blood flow. Once you inhale or exhale, your lungs help the oxygenated or deoxygenated blood get filtered (through those cool little dudes called alveoli). So, all in all, this system is affected largely by our activity. If you're sedentary, your lungs will be more passive and sedentary, as they don't have to do much but the basics. Once you start to challenge your lungs with some active breathing, then you start to work on everything much more. This again takes time for the body to become accustomed to. The more you get them working, like all the other things we've mentioned, the more they will become used to the stress and adapt. Think about this, do all of those instant weight loss programs or short week, thirty-day programs make sense when you start to think about how the body has to adapt to progress?

The other aspect I want to bring to mind is your energy systems. This is quite the complex inner working, so if you want to learn more about how your body produces and uses energy, I would recommend researching and finding good articles that will help explain it much better than I can. What I will tell you is that you have two basic functions when it comes to energy: aerobic and anaerobic. Anaerobic metabolism and energy are done without the presence of oxygen. It depends on stores of fast-acting energy we've built up through glucose (sugar) and certain systems that help it get used quickly. For example, the types of activities that use this energy are fast, like sprinting, HITT workouts, and the like. Aerobic metabolism and energy are the opposite; it is used in the presence of oxygen. So its energy comes from different storages that build up energy for long uses like long-distance running. Two totally different systems, yet the body relies on them to feed us the energy we need to be active.

When you're inactive, your stores of energy are lower, and you won't be able to use them as efficiently or as long as you could if you were consistently active. Again, this is a system that takes time to progress and increase your ability to do activities for longer or more intensely.

The last systems I want to briefly look over are our muscular and skeletal systems (skeletal system provides support for your locomotion and movement). There's so much that goes into these functions in our bodies, but there are only a couple of things I really want you to take away from it. When you challenge your muscles or your skeletal systems, they get stressed by a consistent weight. Now for our systems to overcome that stress and grow from it, they have to have that consistent weight to adapt to and overcome. The more you stress your muscles with a weight, the more they have to grow and get bigger. The more you challenge your skeletal system, the stronger your joints become and become accustomed to stressors.

So all in all, everything that we've talked about and more all take time to get used to exercising and better eating. There's so much I didn't dive into as well that also plays large parts in adapting over time. But the main idea I wanted you to learn is that our bodies are perfectly constructed to thrive in response to what we do with them. So how we eat and what we do will ultimately affect how our bodies can respond. The more active you are, the more your body will respond to being active. The more sedentary you are, the more your body will use less and less energy to fuel certain things. For our health, it's so important to keep things up and running to help us throughout life.

Lifelong Goals

Now that we've talked about the real science of the issue, now you need to understand what a lifelong goal should be. First and foremost, no one talks about lifelong goals today. What's only prevalent is the results now, not later. Think about a young adult that just got a new job out of college. They finally have the income to go out and spend all their money on things they've wanted for so long. That route would be irresponsible, as they would waste their money with nothing to provide for their future. However, let's say a second kid comes around in the same situation, but instead of spending everything he has, he decides to save small portions of it every month. He still has the ability to go out and buy some things that he wants or needs, but down the road later in life, he has built up savings that will better benefit him for his future. That's the same idea with taking care of your body! Think of your body like a bank and healthy nutrition and exercise like money. The more "money" you make, the more that is stored into your bank. The more consistent you put money in the bank, the more you make down the road to use for your future.

When we put effort into taking care of our bodies for the rest of our lives, we will gain so much more down the road. Like I said, no one talks about the importance of the long game in fitness. So when you are deciding to go down this road of healthier living, you need to compare your goals with these tried and true models from ACSM's Resource for a Personal Trainer:

SMALL goals:

» S: Self-selected. Your goals should be your own. Choose goals that fit into your life and only change behaviors that you are willing to negotiate. Remember being realistic, not idealistic, is key.

» M: Measurable. Develop a concrete way to track your goal. Consider the question, "How will I know when my goal has been met?"

» A: Action-oriented. How are you going to achieve your goals? Having an action plan allows you to complete the steps needed to make your goals a reality.

» L: Linked to your life. Goals are best achieved if they work within your lifestyle and match your challenges and strengths. Are your goals designed to fit you and your everyday life?

» L: Long-term. Because you want to be healthy for life, any changes you consider should be something you could see yourself doing for the rest of your life. Create lifestyle-related goals that you feel confident you can maintain.

SMART goals:

» S: Specific. A specific goal should target a specific behavior and include a detailed plan; making a behavior plan is more likely to be implemented than a broad or vague goal.

» M: Measurable. Again, like our SMALL goals, measurable goals are more effective than those that are difficult to quantify.

» A: Achievable. Those that can be achieved and are action-oriented because they target behaviors as opposed to outcomes.

» R: Realistic. Goals that are challenging but achievable are more likely to lead to behavior change and maintenance than unrealistic goals.

» T: Time-oriented. Your goal needs to include a time frame, whether it's short term for certain goals and then long term for others. Allowing a time frame will encourage your progression and consistency to stick to your plan.

At first, it may seem like a lot to try to plan out your goals to these different guidelines, but putting in the effort to make sure that you have a realistic plan of attack will better serve you for a longer period. If you want to be successful in your efforts to change your lifestyle habits, then it's important to put in the work now so that you can make it easy to stick with your routine as you go along. Think back to our bank example. If you had a plan of how much you'd save a month and how much you'd drop into your bank, you would be more consistent and more likely to make that habit instead of just picking a random amount that sounds good and throwing it in your savings. Over time, you may save up some money, but there could be times that you forget to save that money or put less than you should in there. Again, exercise is the same concept as we've said many times. Be consistent, make it a routine, plan it out to the letter, stick with it through the good and the bad, and I think you'll have it made.

Chapter 17

BREAKDOWN OF NUTRITION

"I have the right to do anything," you say—but not everything is beneficial. "I have the right to do anything"—but not everything is constructive. No one should seek their own good, but the good of others. Eat anything sold in the meat market without raising questions of conscience, for, "The earth is the Lord's, and everything in it." If an unbeliever invites you to a meal and you want to go, eat whatever is put before you without raising questions of conscience. But if someone says to you, "This has been offered in sacrifice," then do not eat it, both for the sake of the one who told you and for the sake of conscience. I am referring to the other person's conscience, not yours. For why is my freedom being judged by another's conscience? If I take part in the meal with thankfulness, why am I denounced because of something I thank God for? So whether you eat or drink or whatever you do, do it all for the glory of God. Do not cause anyone to stumble, whether Jews, Greeks or the church of God—even as I try to please everyone in every way. For I am not seeking my own good but the good of many, so that they may be saved.

1 Corinthians 10:23–33

We're finally getting down to the meat and potatoes that are so very misunderstood in the world today (and yes, pun intended). It's time to finally talk, dissect, and discover the honest truths about nutrition and how it works to fuel your body. But first, I want us to start off with some godly thinking that's laid out so nicely for us in 1 Corinthians 10:23–33 from Paul. He's still my favorite writer, and this passage is so good, as it can speak to us on so many levels.

If you read the whole chapter, you'll read that Paul is warning Christians about dabbing into idol worship even being followers of God. Back then, early Christians were toying with the idea that they could still worship idols and God at the same time, but Paul warns them otherwise. Paul then gives examples of the Israelites once they fled Egypt and what happened over many years of their unwise attitudes and idol worship. After Paul gets his point across of the deadly repercussions of tempting a jealous God, he tells the Corinthians they should flee anything that has to do with idols, even food.

This is where I think it gets really interesting in chapter 10. Paul tells the Corinthians that they should be wary about consuming food that was offered for idol worship for the purposes of those who could be watching, both saved and unsaved. This point was to drive home the idea that we should avoid any appearance of worshiping idols, even if that means being wary of certain foods.

The last section of the chapter is a big one that I want you to pay attention to. Paul urges the Corinthians to be restrictive to their rights and freedoms to lead by example so they don't put any stumbling blocks in the way for others. In essence, he is encouraging people to think of what they are doing before they do it and consider if their actions will bring glory to God.

This is critical information we need to take to heart! I listed this large passage of Corinthians to first and foremost give you the correct context of this passage. A lot of "faith and fitness" posts will contain only verse 31, *"So whether you eat or drink or whatever you do, do it all for the glory of God."* Then they will comment how we are to eat well to honor God and so forth. Now please understand me, these concepts are good and have a good message behind them, but I think there's more to offer in this whole passage about encouraging good habits if we look contextually. I know that God breathes His Word to life every day to make it prevalent in what we're going through, and so I have no doubt that there's more here for us to unearth and understand.

First of all, when Paul is explaining how our actions can be a stumbling block for others and their faith, I think we can also make a comparison here with how we treat our bodies and fuel them. Just think about it; your children, friends, and family will see how you treat your body. They will see how you fuel it and use it for God. The way you take care of yourself right now, will people see someone with good self-control that is taking care of what God has given them? Will your family and friends see someone who is doing all of their actions, even when feeding themselves, in a way to honor God? Let me put it this way, when you eat when you're by yourself or comfortable with someone, would you feel like you're honoring God in how you eat? Would you want others from your church to see you eat that way?

It's interesting to think that we could be eating in a way that wouldn't honor God, but it's true.

For example, I remember one time in high school I went on my first "eating out" date with my husband. We were both still in our little giddy butterfly stages, and so it was just so exciting to think about just spending time with each other. I remember, though, that when it came time to eat our food, I was so nervous about how I ate. I wanted to look pristine, perfect, clean, ladylike, and all of the above. Anytime we spoke, I always held my hand in front of my mouth if I was chewing; I always used a napkin every time I took a break from my food, and I was in constant fear of dropping a food particle on my dress. You may not have ever gone to such an extreme, but in one way or another, you've changed how you eat depending on who's around you. There's a way we eat when we're alone (tends to be the method I like to call "ugly eating"), and there's a way we will eat around people whose opinion we care about.

When we are more focused on satisfying our hunger desires no matter what it is, our focus is certainly not on God, and it certainly isn't encouraging those around us. I know there are those of us who become overwhelmed with "hangry" sensations. I know we all get moody when we're really hungry, but think of the opportunity we have to display a loving attitude when we could be the opposite? Would you really risk being a stumbling block for someone else just because you're hungry? Would you want to display such a devotion for bad food that it would make others think it's okay for them to eat that way as well?

What about the type of food you eat? Is the food you're choosing going to encourage someone else to eat well and take care of what they've been given? Or will you encourage bad habits that could cause someone to make food more of an idol like you may do? Oh, here's where we really dive into the fun stuff. People need to realize that today's age has made food an idol to people. No kidding here; we honestly get very connected to food today. Remember back when Popeyes came out with the new chicken sandwich and said it was better than Chick-fil-A's? It was absolute chaos. I remember seeing a line probably a mile's worth from the start of Popeyes drive-through all the way out into the main road. Now don't get me wrong, I get the incentive to try new and fun food. However, when we go great lengths like the whole chicken sandwich debacle, we make food an idol. It's something we must have. Food becomes something we desire more than taking the easy thirty seconds or more to thank God for the meal. Do you see what I mean? Paul is warning us that even with what we eat and drink, we need to be cautious about idols.

God knew before it became an issue that we would struggle with our relationship with food today. He knew that we would be so weak with our self-control that we would struggle with food. Thank goodness He always knows what we need before we need it. God knew we would need this example from Paul to teach us to be aware of how we come across things in our lives and if they do honor God or not. So now, as we dive into the beefy part of nutrition (sorry, I can't stop with the puns), it's time to be honest and vulnerable with God on how you approach your nutrition. Take the time to find where you may let food become your idol and spend that time with God to humble yourself before Him to take those desires away.

Essential Nutritional

Genesis 1:29: *"And God said, Behold, I have given you every herb bearing seed, which is upon the face of all the earth, and every tree, in the which is the fruit of a tree yielding seed; to you it shall be for meat."* When God made the earth and all the things in it, He even made all the different items we would need for food. God knew what items we would need to really fuel our bodies. He didn't just create meat by accident, thinking it would be a nice change in comparison to all the greens He made. He didn't design a fruit tree and then thought it would be nice to have something sweet to eat. He knew we needed essential nutrients to help sustain our bodies through this life. So it should come as no surprise that God designed our bodies to require six essential nutrients that humans need to have to survive and thrive off of.

Nutrients! As I said before, there are six total classes of nutrients to remember: carbohydrates, proteins, fats, vitamins, minerals, and water. Yes, for those of you out there that swear they can't drink water and have to drink something else like sweet tea or lemonade, you too need to realize that water is a nutrient for our body. Six seems like a lot sometimes when we try to cram it all in our day. Well, thankfully, the answer boils down to a simple concept we've applied throughout this book: balance. Balance, as we've said so many times before, is the key and critical to good health and good performance from our bodies.

When we allow one nutrient to take precedence over the others, that is when we can increase the risk of poor health and performance. Here's an example, if you have a low iron intake, it can lead to a lower ability to burn fat. Another example is, let's say you have too much protein to which your body responds by increasing your urine production and making you more dehydrated. It's so fascinating that our bodies know exactly what to do when we have too much or too little. My goodness, our bodies just scream their amazing abilities to their creator, and we never take the time to realize what an amazing mechanism God has granted us to use. So the best strategy to find a balance is to eat a wide variety of foods. Have you ever heard of the food pyramid or My-Plate? They're essentially the same thing that's been changed over the years to teach kids in school the same idea of wide variety. Why? Because studies show us a variety will provide us with a better supply of overall nutrients. Here's the scoop, eat a wide variety, consume fresh fruits and vegetables, and try to avoid eating the same exact thing for several days in a row. Your body changes every day, and so does your nutrient requirement. Kinda crazy how simple it is, isn't it?

Also, something to note that's extremely important: eating a wide variety helps you reduce your chances of consuming potentially toxic nutrients that come from excessively eating possible toxic food components. What I mean is that those foods or supplements that are readily available and inexpensive actually can contain some awful nutrient toxicities. When you eat those types of foods on a regular basis, you dramatically increase your chance of consuming some really horrible toxins for your body. Do you remember the common idea, "If a little bit of this is good for me, why not have more?"? Or the famous line, "Bigger is better!" When it comes to nutrition, and actually several things in this world for that matter, those ideas are actually what has put us in the bad state we are today. When you consume more nutrients than your body can use, it doesn't actually just keep using it. Instead, your body deals with that excess by forcing a cell to excrete the surplus, which forces it to use valuable energy resources. When your cells do this, you increase your risk for developing toxicity reactions or, yes, nutrient sensitivities.

Did any of you ever gorge yourself on a favorite food when you were a kid, and now you can't eat it? Or maybe it doesn't agree with your system anymore? That's me and the candy Twizzlers. That's what can happen when we go a little too crazy on food; our bodies decide they don't want to deal with it anymore and thus, sensitivities. So when you decide to change how you eat, please be aware that even the "good stuff" can be "bad stuff" if you don't balance it well.

When we look at this world, there are so many substances out there now to consume besides our six nutrients, and no surprise here, the majority is not good for you. When man started dabbling in the process of making food last longer, taste better, stay fresher, and the like, the more "stuff" they started putting in there to make that happen. As we tend to do with everything perfect God created from the beginning, we've now turned those six nutrients He designed into this other type of "food" that satisfies us, fattens us, increases our risks for disease, increases rates of obesity, and ultimately destroys our health. Ever heard the saying that if you can't pronounce an ingredient, it's probably not good for you? It's true! It's going to be some sort of additive to make the food last longer or taste better. Notice how you can easily pronounce our six nutrients?

The point of all of this is to drive home the importance of balancing our food and, for some of you, starting to include those six nutrients. Even if you do it in small increments at a time, the point is that it's time to start taking a serious interest in what you're allowing in your body. It's time to start understanding why God made food the way He did and why we need to get back to the basics in food. Next, we're going to dive in depth into our six nutrients so you can understand exactly why we need them.

Functions of Carbohydrates

When it comes down to understanding carbs, they're actually quite complex if you dive deep enough. But what you need to understand is what carbs do for you as a whole:

» They provide energy (specifically four calories per gram of carbs). Carbs are the preferred source of energy for the body, and they're a very quick source as well.

» A concept that is not talked about a lot is carbohydrates are protein sparing. Because carbs are the preferred type of energy source for our body and can meet the requirements the body needs, they will help "spare" protein from being broken down for energy instead.

» *"Oxidation of fat. It has been said that 'fats burn in a carbo-*

hydrate flame.' That is, to burn fats efficiently and completely, some carbohydrates are needed" (Battista 2018, 170). That's a surprise, isn't it? Many people think carbs are "evil" and they only cause weight gain, but the truth is they are essential to weight loss.

» Carbohydrates are actually a very essential component of different compounds in our bodies that we desperately need for our nutrition. Those carbs basically act as a part of other compounds.

» Lastly, carbohydrates help store our energy. Carbs are stored as glycogen, which is one of the best storage forms of energy in our body because it's easily converted into glucose to be readily available for energy.

What those types of carbs do for us is store the energy we need to use to fuel any function in our bodies. Do you know about the keto diet? It's a very popular diet in today's culture, and its basic rules are no carbs (i.e., no sugar or glucose) and only consume fats and proteins. The diet basically makes our systems learn how to function without carbs and only use fats and proteins for fuel; however, no one talks about how hard that switch is on our kidneys, our systems over long-term use, and what the effect can be of limiting our body of a "main ingredient." Remember how carbs can be "protein sparing"? Yeah, there's no sparing any protein on the keto diet.

When people ask me what diet I think is best or what my opinion is on this or that diet, I always return to the idea that if God created carbs, a necessary process our bodies use that He designed from the beginning, then how could a diet be good for you that excludes any of those? Really think about it. I'm not trying to just say that you can only use what God created and nothing else because we know that God has blessed people to invent amazing things that benefit us in many ways. But what I am saying is to think about the basics of food. God created it to work just how our bodies needed it, and now we've changed so many things that we "hope" will work if we just change the whole process. It doesn't make sense to me at all. Why would we want to change something that God knew was perfect from the beginning? Genesis 1:12, "*And the earth brought forth grass, herbs yielding seed after their kind, and trees bearing fruit, wherein is the seed thereof, after their kind: and God saw that it was good.*" He saw that it was good. The food He created for us was beyond a doubt perfect for us. So that makes me think that maybe as a society, we've let our food get out of control, and we need to go back to the basics, back to God's basics.

I also don't state this as just an opinion, but what are the odds that the science points to my conclusion as well? All of the science on what basic nutrition we need to survive and survive well points to our six basic nutrients. From there, studies show us how balance is the key to making everything happy and successful. Yet again, God has planned all of this out to work together, science and all.

Science and studies show that when we are learning how to balance the amount of carbohydrates we consume, the recommendations are *three to twelve grams per kilogram of body weight.* The amount of carbs you do consume does depend on your age, sex, activity, daily expenditure, and environmental conditions. So, for example, let's take a young man that weighed about 160 pounds, which is about seventy-two point five kilograms. Let's also say that he's twenty-five years old and works construction. He would classify as decently active even though he's not working out. This is due to the fact that construction is quite the physical labor, and he's young and has a faster working metabolism at this stage in life. So I would estimate about 8 to 10 grams of carbs per kilogram of his body weight, which equals 580 to 725 grams. Now that's a lot of carbs, but this young man would need that much to provide the energy he needs to have his body perform. Now, these are just estimates because there's only so much that science can actually pinpoint when it comes down to nutrition. So when it comes down to finding out the amount of carbs you need, be honest with how active you are, realistic that you may be a young thing that has a great working metabolism, or maybe you're older, and metabolism isn't as fast as it used to be. When you're plugging in nutrition, you can't "play the system" by plugging in the numbers you wished you had. You will only see results when you finally decide to be honest with yourself about where you're at and plug in the numbers correctly.

Protein

Let's now dive into the information you need to know about protein. Most of us know that protein is good for our bodies and needed to help build muscle. But how many of you really know all of the ways protein helps our bodies? Let's look:

» Proteins are used for enzyme and protein synthesis. What this means is that the hundreds of unique tissues we have in our bodies and enzymes are actually made up of protein.

» A huge job for protein is transporting our nutrients to the correct places in our bodies. Basically, protein creates these "carriers" that help take nutrients to and fro to the right tissues.

» This may surprise some of you, but protein is actually a source of energy. There is a portion of carbon in protein that provides our bodies with the same energy we get from carbs, four calories per gram.

» Yay, hormones! Ladies, don't roll your eyes; it's not the kind you're thinking of. There are many hormones we actually need to thrive on, and thankfully, protein helps with the production of certain hormones. For example, protein helps with hormones because it helps with building the hormone testosterone (the male hormone). Protein helps with several vital hormones for men and women that we would struggle without the production of.

» Protein helps with the fluid balance in our bodies. Specifically, it helps with the balance between our blood and surrounding tissue as well as maintaining blood volume and sweat rates during physical activities.

» This is a fun one; protein helps with keeping a good acid-base balance. Pretty much this means that protein helps make an acidic-like environment less acidic, even an alkaline environment less alkaline. This can be seen where protein helps buffer the buildup of lactic acid (that really harsh burning feeling you can get when you start to exercise pretty hard and the soreness afterward).

» This one is obvious, but protein helps with our growth and tissue maintenance. Protein is a must if we are to build and maintain our tissue. Of course, we think of protein as necessary if we're trying to build muscle, but think of how vital it would be for children and seniors. It helps with growth, which is so important for kids, and tissue maintenance, which is something people lose as they age.

» Lastly, protein helps with the synthesis of a nonprotein compound that contains nitrogen. What this compound does is help release a high-energy amount of nitrogen to be used for a quick burst of activity. When a child decides to start sprinting in the park, his protein helps activate that compound to give him energy. Pretty cool, huh?

There's a lot I could go into when it comes to protein, but as said before, I just want to keep it to the basics. Everyone and their mom are going to have an opinion on protein and how much you should take. I want to suggest sticking to the recommendations that several very smart scientists and studies have proven.

Recommended intakes:

» Infants: two point two grams per kilogram of body weight a day

» Children: one to one point six grams per kilogram of body weight a day

» Adults: zero point eight grams per kilogram of body weight a day

» Adult athletes: one point two to one point seven grams per kilogram of body weight a day

You'll notice that the adults' recommendation is lower than any other category. That's because that suggestion is geared towards more sedentary adults. Infants and children have a lot of growing to do as well as being more active than the average adult. Most adults are not active enough to require more protein unless they are an athlete or are exercising regularly. So when you're plugging in your protein amounts, be sure to plug in the right amount no matter where you're starting. Let me say this; it does not benefit you to take more protein than you need. Our culture has now taught us to believe that more of a good thing will help us. This is so very wrong when it comes to nutrition. When we consume more nutrients than we need, a couple of things happen: Our cells will expend precious energy to get rid of the extra nutrients; our body pushes the nutrients (specifically protein) out through urination, which dehydrates us; our bodies keep the extra amount into our "backup" storage (which is how we build fat, the bad kind). This is only a very basic list. Do some research on your own about what happens when you take too much of a nutrient. The effects are kind of daunting. That's why it's so important to try to balance how much you eat of each nutrient. But also, please don't start to worry about not being exact with your food. Unless you have the drive to weigh out your food every single time you eat (I have never had that energy in my entire health career), just be sure to be aware of how much protein you have versus carbs versus fats and that kind of thing. Shortly, we'll dive into how I suggest balancing everything in a flexible and easy way!

Fat

Fat is my favorite to talk about because it's most everyone's least favorite. For some reason, we have decided that "fat" is bad because it's also the term of the literal buildup of fat in our bodies. Why the scientists that discovered fat in our bodies also had to name a nutrient fat has always puzzled me. Here's the truth, fat is good for you! Yay! We need to stop this obsessing that our society has started that anything with fat is bad. There is a way to eat too much and the wrong kind, for sure. However, as it should not be a surprise, God created the nutrient fat for some very important reasons, and we should always be conscious of including it into our daily diets.

» Good news: Fat is a source of energy. It actually contains a whopping nine calories per gram, much more than the four calories from carbs and proteins.

» Fat is a wonderful engineered survival tool that helps provide insulation against extreme temperatures as well as protect our bodies from concussive forces.

» The next thing that I love about fat is that it's our satiety control. What this means is that fat is what actually helps us feel fuller longer. Fat stays in our stomachs longer than any other nutrient. So when you want to fuel yourself with something that will stick with you, consider finding a little bit of fat to include in there.

» Fat is the wonderful carrier of essential nutrients. It also contains some key fat-soluble vitamins like A, D, E, and K.

» Lastly, fat gives food flavor! That's right; fat is what makes our food tasty.

I remember listening to Mark Lowry, the stand-up comedian for Gaither Vocal Band. One day, he talked about how he felt much more comfortable holding fat babies compared to skinny babies. If he were to drop a skinny baby, he was always afraid they'd break, whereas a fat baby would bounce. While I implore you to never try that at all, as he meant it as a joke, there's some minor truth to his statement. While fat doesn't make us "bounce," it sure does help us rebound easier, if you will, from an outside force. My point is that fat is so important for us to include in our daily nutrition. I promise you that fats are friends, not foes.

When it comes down to how much fat we should consume, this is where I encourage you to really pay attention. The current guidelines for fat intake are between 20 percent and 35 percent of your total calories. I would say that most people actually benefit a lot better from doing no more than 25 percent of their total calories because you will soon realize that it can be a challenge to balance your fat intake. So, for example, a person who weighs about 165 pounds or seventy-five kilograms will consume around 3,000 calories a day. If you took about 25 percent of that amount of calories for fat, you would need to consume about 750 calories from fat. Again, this may be a shock to some of you, as you may have had the mindset for so long that fat is bad for you. Think again, God knew we would need it to survive, so it's very important for our nutrition.

What you really need to know about fat is that there are good kinds and bad kinds, and no surprise here, our current world *thrives* on the bad kind.

Good fats:

» Polyunsaturated fatty acids—found in vegetable oil and cereal oil like corn oil. Have lots of vitamin E and have a tendency to lower blood cholesterol levels.

» Monounsaturated fatty acids—found in olive oil and canola oil, can help lower blood cholesterol levels while maintaining your high-density lipoprotein (your good cholesterol).

» High-density lipoproteins—carry lipids away from storage and take them to your liver for metabolism and possible excretion (the good cholesterol since it helps remove cholesterol).

» If a fat is liquid at room temperature rather than solid, it is more than likely a good fat, like oils. Certain natural foods like seeds, vegetables, fruits (avocados), and fish all contain healthy fats.

Bad fats:

> » Saturated fatty acids—increase serum cholesterol, found in meats and dairy products.

> » Low-density lipoproteins—this is the major carrier of your cholesterol and other lipids in your blood (the bad kind basically installs cholesterol in you).

> » If the fat is a solid instead of a liquid, it is most likely a saturated fat like margarine or butter.

> » Bad fats also are the key culprits in most processed foods that help preserve the shelf life.

Vitamins and Minerals

Lastly, I want to talk about the three important nutrients that are more commonly left in the dust. A vast majority of people do not include enough vitamins, minerals, and water in their everyday lives. For some reason, we've given those three nutrients little thought when it comes to our health, which is quite frankly bizarre, as they are key components to good health. Now I don't want to bore you or make this subject complicated, so I'm just going to give you the very basics on what they do for you and where you can find them. I encourage you to do your own research on vitamins and minerals you know that you may be lacking in and see what happens when you have a deficiency in it and how you can find ways to include foods that will include those nutrients.

Let's first dive into talking about vitamins. You've probably heard that you need to take your daily vitamins, but has anyone really told you why? Why do you need those daily vitamins, and what do they actually do for you? Well, to be quite honest, all vitamins will benefit you in some shape or form, but there are a couple of essential ones that I want to encourage you to start being mindful to include in your nutrition:

» Vitamin C—this is no surprise, but it's nonetheless important. Vitamin C is known for being an antioxidant, helping with collagen formation and iron absorption, good carnitine synthesis, and norepinephrine synthesis. Basically, it's going to help your overall immune system. You can find ample amounts of vitamin C in fresh fruits and vegetables, especially very high citrus fruits.

» Vitamin B—there are several different hats that Vitamin B wears, as it contains many different forms that are important for us: thiamin (B1), riboflavin (B2), niacin (B3), pantothenic acid (B5), pyridoxal (B5), cobalamin (B12), biotin, and folate/folic acid. To make it simple, B is responsible for the oxidation of fats and carbs, good eye function, healthy skin and hair and nails, good nerve conduction, healthy bones, and, honestly, the inner workings of your body if you have a good, wide variety of foods like different lean meats, dairy, grains, seeds, and eggs.

» Vitamin A—this vitamin helps with our vision, growth, reproduction, good immune function, and healthy skin. You can find

A in foods like dark green leafy vegetables, yellow vegetables, fruit, fortified margarine, milk, and egg yolk.

» Vitamin D—most of us were told to drink milk for vitamin D so we could grow strong bones. That's true; vitamin D helps us with our skeletal system but also plays a part in cardiovascular health and a healthy immune system. We can find D in milk and sunlight (fifteen minutes), and small amounts have been found in egg yolk, butter, liver, and canned salmon and sardines.

» Vitamin E—this guy is a powerful antioxidant as well as another important helper with a good immunity. You can find E in vegetable oils, leafy green vegetables, nuts, and even legumes.

» Vitamin K—This tends to surprise some people, but K is important for helping our blood to clot. Isn't that a bad thing? Not when we're talking about relying on our body to help clot blood on a scrap or a cut that will allow the blood to stop, eventually healing itself. K is found in, again, dark leafy green vegetables.

Now let's discuss our minerals, shall we? Basically, minerals are going to cover the other areas of bodily function that vitamins do not. They are responsible for water balance, nerve impulse stimulation, acid-base balance, and energy reactions. If that doesn't quite make sense, that's okay. Sometimes I have to Google what "acid-base balance" is because it's definitely not the verbal jargon I use in everyday life. But let me just show you what is important for you to understand:

» Calcium—this is a big one that most of us know helps keep our bones strong. Did you also know, however, it helps with blood coagulation, nerve impulse transmission, and muscle contraction? Super important for our bodies to have! You can get good calcium in food items like milk and other dairy sources, dark green leafy vegetables, canned fish (with bones).

» Phosphorus—yet another "bone mineral," as it helps with the structure of our bones and teeth. Also helps with some more complicated functions like DNA and RNA, has parts of many vitamin B coenzymes, and is a component of our energy compound called ATP (adenosine triphosphate). Don't worry; I won't be testing you on that.

» Iron—this one is huge! Most people lack iron, which can cause less energy, easy fatigue, anemia, even lead to weakness. If we get iron into our system, however, it helps with oxygen transfer to cells and lots of oxidative enzymes. You can find plenty of iron in meats like poultry and fish, egg yolk, and even some in dark leafy green vegetables, legumes, peaches, apricots, prunes, raisins, and legumes.

» Zinc—big helper in bettering our immune system, wound healing, and even helping with enzymes that are involved in energy metabolism. Found commonly in these foods: seafood, meat, wheat germ, yeast, and I must tell you that most plant food sources are not good sources for iron. For those of you pursuing a vegetarian diet, please be aware you may need to seek supplements.

» Magnesium—the biggest issue of not consuming this mineral is it leads to muscle weakness. If you do take it, it helps with good energy metabolism of carbs and fats, protein synthesis, water balance, and muscle contractions. It's actually found commonly in many foods, but the highest containers of magnesium are meats, whole grains, seeds, and legumes.

Again, this is just touching the tip of the iceberg when it comes to your vitamins and minerals, but what I wanted to share was the importance of them. Now you know the most vital, and I hope you take some time to reevaluate your vitamin and mineral situation. Did you notice that many of the foods that naturally have these nutrients are what would be included in a wide variety of food? This was no surprise to God when He created nutrition for us! He's like our own personal chef that knows exactly what we need. He made it so easy to obtain foods that are good for us that will not only help feed us but make certain areas of our body function better. Just to be clear, I promise you that you will find the slightest amount of vitamins and minerals, if any, in processed food. It just makes more sense to eat healthily, doesn't it?

Water

This isn't big news. You know that you're supposed to drink water. I'm sure you've had a friend, relative, or some sort of health professional get on to you about drinking water. I know I did in the past. Here's the thing, this amazing resource of hydration that was here when the earth was created (again, God planned that) we now think is too "tasteless" or just not as fun to drink, so we don't. Do you want to know what happens to your body when you don't hydrate it? Well, here you go. Our bodies are made up of about 60 percent water. That's right. When we fail to provide enough water, our bodies will go into failure, which can cause death. Not that I'm saying that only drinking a cup or so every day is going to cause death, but I want to show you how vital it is for us. Water is what keeps our bodies functioning and living, no joke. It is the most vital nutrient that our bodies need, and yet the amount of people that actually drink water consistently is alarmingly low.

Well, if there's so much water in our bodies, how do we even become dehydrated? Good question. We lose our water through breathing (our breath is moist), through sweat (even if there's none visible, you're still sweating out the water), urinating, actually visible sweat through activity, and feces. So even if you're a couch potato, you're still going to lose water because it's required in our daily bodily functions. So yes, you must drink water, and I want to encourage you to drink more than you normally do.

I didn't start noticing how little water I drank until I started college and was attending my nutrition classes. Suddenly, I realized that I was very poorly hydrating myself, and my body was the one taking the consequences. It wasn't easy at first. Yes, I had to go all the time. It was a pain to carry around my water bottle everywhere and track how much I drank. You know what is interesting, though? I started to notice some differences in my body. I noticed my skin was happier (fewer breakouts and smoother). I felt better, more energized. After my workouts, I didn't feel like dying; I actually felt good, and even my muscles seemed to be less sore. I just felt better overall! I then decided to test this newfound result. I went one day without pushing my water as I normally did. Let me tell you, I felt *horrible*. I had a massive headache; I was sluggish; I felt gross all over, and I didn't even want to leave my house. The next day, I immediately grabbed my water bottle and didn't look back. For almost six years now, I have brought my water bottle with me everywhere I go. It's almost like a companion for me at this point. But I know that I function so much better when I stay hydrated, and you will, too, if you just try.

Let's review what water can do for us: It helps lower blood pressure, transports oxygen, makes skin happy and healthy, gives us energy, helps flush out waste and harmful particles, helps kidney function, transports minerals and nutrients, helps your digestive system, and even can help regulate your body temperature. The benefits of water are actually a very long list, but I think with just the basics, I've proven my point. Your body needs it, and it's time to take drinking seriously, water that is.

How much should I drink? Good question. Well, first and foremost, don't rely on drinking only when your body tells you're thirsty, as the sensation occurs when you've already lost about one to two percent of body weight. It's easier to think of drinking water in time intervals instead. I tell my clients that I plan to have a certain amount of water drank before noon so that I know I'm on pace for the rest of the day. The current guidelines for water are as follows: thirteen cups (a little less than a gallon) for men and about nine cups (just over half of a gallon) for women. This is just a starting number, however. Water is dependent on your size, metabolism, diet, physical activity, and health factors. Also, if you're maybe drinking only one solid cup of water a day, those numbers might be intimidating. The best route is to introduce it slowly. If you only drink two cups of water a day now, I would encourage you to try three or four. Once that gets comfortable, then try another cup or two. Before you know it, your body will be used to the amount of water, and it won't be so hard to increase it in small amounts. You also need to make sure you fit the amount of water to what your daily life revolves around. If you're very active, then you may need more than the recommended amount, but if you're not, then maybe stick with the general recommendation. Lastly, if you're a part of the census that doesn't like the taste of water, I would suggest looking into doing fruit or vegetable flavored water. You can simply cut up a fruit that you like and let it sit in your water so that it has a wonderful fruity flavor. There are all sorts of recipes you can Google to find one you like. I do recommend staying away from water-flavoring powders as they tend to have more junk in them than good stuff. That's it! I promise you won't regret learning how to drink enough water; it will change your life.

Putting It All Together

That's it; you know the basics of food that will get you further than any diet program out there. It may seem like a lot of information. For those of you that thought this was a slight overload, don't worry. I'm done teaching you the "science" of nutrition. I make it a point to teach all my clients the basics of nutrition because hardly anyone really understands how food works, and I think for people to really understand how to fuel their bodies well, they need to understand what it does for them. I think nowadays we tend to be a little lazy when it comes to health. Instead of trying to find out information on food and exercise itself, we now resort to just buying expensive diet or exercise plans. I'm not saying that finding resources that can help you is bad if you don't have the time yourself, but if you're that passionate about changing your current circumstances, nothing will fuel you to change like if you truly understand what's happening. What we need to talk about now is how to put all of this together so that you can be confident in what you know so that, first and foremost, you fuel your body correctly. Secondly, avoid those fad diets and gimmicks out there that try to just get money with no results. Lastly, encourage those around you by living a healthier life for God. Let's call it the SIMPLE process.

S—Start discovering fad diets and other "instant weight loss" gimmicks. Rule of thumb, if it sounds too good to be true, then it is. There's no magical fruit, pill, or food combination that we've suddenly just discovered that's going to make you lose weight. When something is trying to lure you in by saying it's the "newest and greatest discovery," run the other way. All of those types of "instant weight loss" things are placebos (they don't work at all but make you hope that they do), or they're a super restrictive and unrealistic diet. But why are there so many diets out there that people claim to have lost weight? Well, the truth is that they have lost weight, but nobody talks about how long they kept the weight off or what their lifestyle was compared to yours.

I—Is it realistic? Looking at the reality of a diet is one of the key components I teach every client that comes my way. If you were the Rock (Dwayne Johnson, big movie star and large muscular man), then you would have the resources to pay for all the crazy health food to always be at your fingertips. You would also have the time to dedicate to fixing the food a certain way, eating a certain amount consistently, working out all the time, and maintaining that same schedule for several years. People like Mr. Rock have that ability to follow crazy programs because they either have a lot of money to make it happen, it's their job to look that way, or they can hire someone to help them stay consistent. What I'm trying to teach you is for the average folks. I'm talking to a family of five that's constantly going and has hardly any time to even breathe. I'm talking to the busy businessman or woman that's so invested in a career that's also trying to figure out how to invest in their health. I'm talking to you, whatever your situation may be, that it is possible to become healthy without having to go down the road of hundreds of dollars and crazy schedules.

M—Make it easy. Don't make your life absolutely miserable trying to get back into shape. As Solomon tells us in Ecclesiastes 2, verse 24, *"There's nothing better for a man than that he should eat and drink, and that he should make his soul enjoy good in his labor. I also saw that it was from the hand of God."* Solomon is telling us that nothing in this life will fulfill us until we start to live a life in obedience to God in which He has blessed us with a life to enjoy. As we've discussed before, you shouldn't be chasing after a healthier life that this world promotes; you should be pursuing a healthier life because you want to serve God. I promise you that taking the time to enjoy life and slowly allowing yourself to change bad habits will make life easier. Not only will life be easier, but you can actually enjoy it like God intended. Because you take the time to do it the right way, you will find more enjoyment in what you're doing, "*...he should make his soul enjoy...his labor.*" God has created us to find enjoyment in this life when we do it in obedience to Him.

I'm going to tell you something that most diets will completely disagree with me on. When you're craving some junk food, when you're invited out with friends at a restaurant, your kids want to get some ice cream, go do it. Don't limit yourself so much that you miss out on fun memories. The worst thing you can do for yourself is limit all the fun foods you love so much that one day you will break your resistance and go crazy. You will burn out if you go that route. Instead, if you have a craving, then be mindful of how much and how often you partake. I always have a sweet craving pop up, so if I really don't want to walk away, then I'll let myself enjoy something small and reasonable and then make sure I stay consistent with my better foods for the rest of the week. Go out with those friends on Wednesday night, but then maybe try to be a little more conscious of your foods for the rest of the week. If you make your life miserable, you will be miserable. But if you let yourself enjoy those good things with self-control, you will enjoy learning to eat healthily. So instead of going at the world's crazy, unrealistic pace that won't pay off in the end, take the time to enjoy the journey God has laid before you.

P—Praise God for each step you're able to take. Most of the time, we forget to be grateful for what we have right now. Have you thought about the resources you have to feed yourself and your family? It's pretty incredible how God can provide, even if we think we should be doing better. No matter what stage you're in, there's always something to be grateful for. So as you start planning out to change around your nutrition, be grateful that He's allowing you the passion to do so, the opportunity, and the resources to do so. Not only that, I always try to remind myself that I need to thank God for the body He gave me. I have the ability to walk, run, and be active, whereas I know that not all can. That's a huge blessing, and it's not something we should take lightly or abuse; that's why I believe with all my heart that it's so important to take care of what you have.

E—Essentials. When it comes to learning and adjusting to new nutritional habits, the best way I have found to think about it is sticking to the essentials. You now know what nutrients you need in your daily food, but now is the time to stick to a routine to overcome the tempting junk food that is ever-present. When I'm tempted with sweets or something that I know is not good for me, I always think back to how I don't want to let food rule my life. "*All things are lawful unto me, but all things are not expedient: all things are lawful for me, but I will not be brought under the power of any*" (1 Corinthians 6:12). I don't want to be under the "power" of food. It may be silly to think of, but there are times when I have to stop and pray to ask for strength to avoid food that I know will give me no benefit. It may seem like something small

306

to ask, but the Lord says, "*If you abide in me, and my words abide in you, ask whatever you wish, and it will be done for you*" (John 15:7). The Lord tells us to live this life in obedience to Him and tell Him the desires of our hearts. There is no one thing that the Lord doesn't already know that's going on in your life, and if that one thing is your struggle with food, then don't feel ashamed to admit your weakness to Him. God didn't design us to be gluttons of anything in this world, not even food. So when you're struggling, take a moment to ask for help. When it comes down to deciding what the essentials are that I need for food, I always think back to what that food is. For example, let's say you pick up an apple and are thinking if you should eat it. There are no processed foods in that apple; it's just purely *an apple.* However, if you were to pick up a candy bar, you would find that a candy bar is not just merely a candy bar. It's milk chocolate, artificial flavors, enriched wheat flour, and a bunch of ingredients I can't pronounce. I had a college professor tell me in a nutrition class that if you can't pronounce the ingredient, it's most likely not natural and probably isn't good for you. So go with the essentials, the food that is what it says it is. Stick with good ol' fruits, vegetables, meats, grains, oils, and dairy. Those will be the most beneficial to you when you compare them to all of the other junk that's in today's world.

That's my SIMPLE method. It's not complex; it doesn't cost you hundreds and hundreds of dollars, but it is simple. I think that's how nutrition should be. Food shouldn't have to be this stressful, complex thing that rules our lives. The "health" industry today throws pills after diets after cleanse that's guaranteed to make you lose weight.

Well, if you're going to live off of only water for three days, then sure, you're going to lose some weight (that's no joke; that's a real cleanse). If you're going to pick an extreme diet that cuts out major carbs and calories, you will lose some weight. What all of these things have in common is a calorie deficiency. That's the "key" to any diet you look at, no matter how it claims to be "different." Keto diet—cuts out carbs which is a source of calories. Whole30 diet—cutting out bad foods in your diet, a.k.a., cutting out some calories but only for thirty days. Oh, you might get some results, but what happens when you hop back into your normal routine? That weight is going to pop right back up. Vegan and vegetarian diets—some people have to go this route for health reasons, but it also cuts out calories by cutting out animal products. Are you noticing a pattern yet? You can Google all the hundreds (and yes, there are hundreds) of diets, and they will all "leave" out something that will help with cutting calories. How is it that there are hundreds of diets, but yet not one works for everyone? Honestly, the majority are just out there to make money, and those that actually try to help are never realistic for everyday people.

I'm going to leave it at that. I've told you what I know. I'm not a licensed nutritionist, so I can't tell you how to make a meal plan. But I can tell you how food works, how to weed out the fads, and what necessary information you need to be able to understand what foods you need to properly fuel yourself. Don't let this world run your life, but instead, take joy in knowing you can take back your health.

Chapter 18

COMBINING FAITH AND FITNESS

As for other matters, brothers and sisters, we instructed you how to live in order to please God, as in fact you are living. Now we ask you and urge you in the Lord Jesus to do this more and more. For you know what instructions we gave you by the authority of the Lord Jesus. It is God's will that you should be sanctified: that you should avoid sexual immorality; that each of you should learn to control you own body in a way that is holy and honorable, not in passionate lust like the pagans, who do not know God; and that is this matter no one should wrong or take advantage of a brother or a sister. The Lord will punish all those who commit such sins, as we told you and warned you before. For God did not call us to be impure, but to live a holy life. Therefore, anyone who rejects this instruction does not reject a human being but God, the very God who gives you his Holy Spirit. Now about your love for one another we do not need to write to you, for you yourselves have been taught by God to love each other. And in fact, you do love all of God's family throughout Macedonia. Yet we urge you, brothers and sisters, to do so more and more, and to make it your am-

bition to lead a quiet life: You should mind your own business and work with your hands, just as we told you, so that your daily life may win the respect of outsiders and so that you will not be dependent on anybody.

1 Thessalonians 4:1–12

When Paul was writing to the Thessalonian believers, he was instructing on how they should live their personal lives in purity and with godly behavior. God knew we all needed to hear this passage, as the areas Paul mentions are ones we all struggle with throughout our life. He knew that we would need instruction on how to live a holy life. Paul teaches that we are to avoid sexual immorality, love one another, live a peaceful life while keeping to ourselves, and work to provide for our needs. These areas all show something that is so important in our walks of faith: a good testimony. Paul is challenging these people to be the godly people that God has asked them to be by living an exemplary life. Living this way not only is obedient to God, but it provides evidence to non-believers about the power of our Lord in our own lives. Through living a godly life, we can impact those around us.

I know I needed to hear this passage today. I needed to be reminded that God has not just simply put us on this earth to "be here." He has designed each and every one of us for a purpose and has given us the tools to do His will. As we are now nearing the end of this book, I want to remind you of the same. God has not simply just given you a body. He has given you your body. He has given you your abilities. He has a plan for you. God has given us instructions on how to live our lives for Him, and He has pressed us to use our bodies in a way that is holy and honorable. We have been tasked to work with our own hands. To be dependent on ourselves and, of course, fully dependent on God and no one else. I've talked to you throughout this entire book about how to use your body in a way that will honor God. And now we've come to the point where you have to decide, are you going to take what you've learned and start to change your physical lifestyle to be one that is godly? Or will you continue to let this world run your body for you? I know which way I want to go; I know the conviction I've had in my heart about using my body for God's purposes, and I pray you have the same.

Let God Be First in Your Plan

We've talked a lot about making sure that Christ is your focus in your healthy living goals. Now that you know all the intricacies of exercise, nutrition, and all of the other stuff, don't forget where your focus should really lie.

When I realized and set to action my newfound "godly goals" of exercise, the first week was good. I was trying to keep my heart focused on working on my body so that God could use it. I would thank Him after every exercise for the body He gave me and be grateful for where I currently was and how He was challenging me to improve. I felt myself thriving like never before because I really had a passion for exercising "right" this time. It didn't take long, however; soon, I began really getting into my workouts so much that I started to have tunnel vision. Soon it was about how much weight I could lift, where I saw muscle appearing, what clothes fit me best, what music I was listening to that would motivate me the most. I soon was obtaining comments from fellow gym rats that would praise me on my growth. I was glowing with pride, and I had no idea that even though I had "gained" more than I had ever done in my life, I had lost what was truly important. I lost my focus to serve God. I realized that I couldn't teach others about serving God if I couldn't even do it myself. I felt like I was punched in the gut. I had worked on my body for about two years to get it to the point it was at, but none of it mattered because I was chasing after worldly things. I felt the pull, the temptation, or even, if you will, a resistance beyond this world that was trying to convince me to stay the course. I felt my flesh deeply desire the life I lived in the gym, and it didn't want me to give it up.

Let me tell you, as healthy living is what my dreams have evolved around for years, it hurt to see that so quickly I had fallen in step with the sinful desires of my heart. One day, I knew exactly what I needed to do. For the record, I don't like to act without thinking something through. I want to plan it out, talk with my husband about it; I aspire to always pray about it (I'm still growing in that area), and then make my decision. But part of me knew that if I took the time to think about whether or not to continue my current lifestyle, I wouldn't be strong enough to step away. So a couple of weeks later, I called the gym and canceled my membership. A month later, I lost about fifteen pounds of muscle that I had spent over two years building. It was a different experience, let me tell you. I had this strange feeling of loss as I let that part of me go. But as soon as I stopped going to the gym for those two long hours every day, I suddenly found more time to spend with God. I was spending the time in my devotions that I had rushed before. Through the time with God, I began to feel my heart change towards fitness. I wanted to stay healthy; I wanted to be usable for Christ, but I was not about to let the fitness world rule me.

So I decided to start working out at home. Create my own home gym, which I wanted so it would keep me in check with being obsessed with gaining muscle. It may sound a little silly, but I really was. So now I'm not as muscular as I was, but I'm still healthy and fit. And every time I work out, I always try to remember to spend time in prayer during my stretches to thank God for changing my heart, for showing me what He wanted for my body, and for what He's given me. As you start out, I implore you to not get "caught up" in the success you will find. I promise you'll find success if you can stick with the X, Y, and Z I have given you. I ask you to make sure and be thankful for what you have, what you are given, and to never let your health journey become more important than the Lord Almighty. Don't forget the real reason we should improve our health, to become living sacrifices for Him.

I want you to be the "salt and light" in the health world. Be that light others need to show them God's work in your life.

You are the salt of the earth. But if the salt loses its saltiness,
how can it be made salty again? It is no longer good for any-

thing except to be thrown out and trampled underfoot. You are the light of the world. A town built on a hill cannot be hidden. Neither do people light a lamp and put it under a bowl. Instead they put it on its stand, and it gives light to everyone in the house. In the same way, let your light shine before others, that they may see your good deeds and glorify your Father in heaven.

Matthew 5:13–14

You have the unique ability to be light in a place where there are so few. Go out and reach those around you for the glory of God. Nothing you gain, whether it be muscle, losing weight, becoming healthier, will be worth anything unless you use it for the will of God.

My friends, take this time to pray with me as you set out on this new adventure in your life: *Father in heaven, please direct and guide me in this new journey of taking care of the body You have given me. Remind me to be grateful for what I do have and let me be thankful for the ways I can improve myself. Let me not be tempted or distracted by worldly things that will only pass away but instead let my focus stay on You. As I grow, let me first grow my faith in You. As I get stronger, give me the wisdom to remember that You are the only strength I need. As I become able to go places I couldn't before, it softens my heart to go out to love those around me instead of myself. I want to use this body as a living sacrifice for You. Give me the strength today to be consistent, dedicated, and mindful as I start down this road. I give my heart, my life, and my body to You to use. Amen.*

NOTES

Preface

   1. Romans 12:1–2 (NIV).

Introduction

   1. Romans 6:12–13 (The Voice).

   2. Matthew 28:19–20 (The Voice).

Chapter 1: A Perfect Plan

   1. Jeremiah 1:5 (ESV).

   2. Ephesians 2:1–10 (The Voice).

   3. Genesis 1:31 (KJV).

   4. Philippians 4:8 (NIV).

   5. James 1:2–18 (ESV).

   6. Genesis 1:26 (KJV).

   7. Psalm 139:14 (ESV).

Chapter 2: A Content Heart

   1. Luke 12:13–21 (ESV).

2. 1 Timothy 6:6–9 (NIV).

3. Matthew 5:48 (ESV).

4. Psalm 139:14 (ESV).

5. Ephesians 2:10 (ESV).

6. Genesis 1:27 (ESV).

7. 2 Corinthians 12:9 (ESV).

8. Matthew 16:26 (NIV).

9. Galatians 5:16–21 (The Voice).

10. Galatians 5:22 (The Voice).

Chapter 3: Being a Good Steward

1. Matthew 25:20–21 (ESV).

2. See Matthew 25:14–30.

3. Nimtz, Eric. "Using Our Talents." November 21, 2021. https://copperfield.church/resources/livestream/.

4. Romans 8:3–8 (NIV).

5. Romans 12:2 (ESV).

6. Ephesians 5:11 (ESV).

7. 1 Thessalonians 5:18 (ESV).

8. 1 Corinthians 6:19 (ESV).

9. 1 Corinthians 4:1–2 (KJV).

10. Rethink Obesity. "Obesity is a Chronic and Progressive Disease." 2021. https://www.rethinkobesity.com/

disease-progression.html?&utm_source=bing&utm_medium=cpc&utm_term=what%20causes%20obesity&utm_campaign=4_Phrase_Shared_UB_Diagnosis&utm_content=-dc_pcrid_73736254022424_pkw_what%20causes%20obesity_pmt_bp_slid__&msclkid=baa82a.

11. Mark 12:31 (ESV).

12. Proverbs 27:17 (KJV).

13. Proverbs 27:6 (KJV).

14. Matthew 5:14–16 (NIV).

15. Revelation 22:17 (The Voice).

Chapter 4: God's View of a Healthy Lifestyle

1. Galatians 5:22–23 (NIV).

2. R., Pam. "Self-Control." Last modified October 29, 2021. https://afaithinprocess.com/self-control/.

3. Titus 2:11–13 (NIV).

4. Diamond, Anna. "A Crispy, Salty, American History of Fast Food." Last modified June 24, 2019. https://www.smithsonianmag.com/history/crispy-salty-american-history-fast-food-180972459/.

5. Philippians 3:19 (NIV).

6. Romans 13:14 (NIV).

7. Proverbs 23:20–21 (NIV).

8. 1 Timothy 4:7–8 (NASB).

9. See 1 Corinthians 9:25.

10. 1 Corinthians 10:13 (NIV).

11. Philippians 4:13 (KJV).

12. Colossians 3:17 (KJV).

13. Tebow, Tim. *This is the Day: Reclaim Your Dream. Ignite Your Passion. Live Your Purpose.* N.p.: WaterBrook, 2018, 122–125.

Chapter 5: Finding Wisdom in Fitness

1. Ecclesiastes 2:1–7, 9–11, 24–26 (NIV).

2. See John 4:14.

3. Romans 12:2 (ESV).

4. Matthew 5:28 (ESV).

5. See 1 John 1:1.

6. Volley-Pedia. "What is a Libero?" Accessed January 31, 2022. https://www.volley-pedia.com/libero.

7. 2 Peter 1:5–9 (The Voice).

8. Psalm 63:1 (ESV).

9. Matthew 5:14–16 (NIV).

Chapter 6: Seeing Past False Promises

1. 2 Timothy 4:1–5 (NIV).

2. 2 Timothy 4:7 (NIV).

3. 2 Timothy 4:3–4 (NIV).

4. Luke 12:22–34 (NIV).

Chapter 7: Hard Work Means Hard Work

1. Proverbs 13:4–11 (NIV).

2. IMDb. "WALL·E (2008)—Plot Summary." Accessed January 31, 2022. https://www.imdb.com/title/tt0910970/plotsummary.

3. WHO | World Health Organization. "Obesity and overweight." Last modified June 9, 2021. https://www.who.int/news-room/fact-sheets/detail/obesity-and-overweight.

4. Abdelaal, Mahmoud, Carel W. le Roux, and Neil G. Docherty. "Morbidity and Mortality Associated with Obesity." Annals of Translational Medicine, April 2017. http://dx.doi.org/10.21037/atm.2017.03.107.

5. Psalm 90:12 (NIV).

6. Isaiah 64:8 (ESV).

7. Psalm 128:1–2 (ESV).

8. 1 John 2:3–6 (KJV).

9. 1 John 2:4 (KJV).

10. Revelation 3:15–16 (ESV).

11. See 1 John 2:3–4.

12. Eric Liddell Center. "Biography." N.d. https://www.ericliddell.org/biography/.

13. Ephesians 2:1–10 (NIV).

14. Galatians 6:7 (NIV).

15. John 15:19 (NLT).

Chapter 8: Accountability = Success

1. Galatians 6:1–9 (NIV).

2. 1 John 4:11 (KJV).

3. Desmond Doss. "The Real Story." Accessed January 31, 2022. https://desmonddoss.com/bio/bio-real.php.

Chapter 9: Behavior Change Is a Must

1. 1 Corinthians 10:13 (ESV).

2. Philippians 4:13 (KJV).

3. Tervooren, Tyler. "Internal vs. External Motivation: How to Build an Exercise Routine You'll Stick To." HuffPost, March 26, 2015. https://www.huffpost.com/entry/internal-vs-external-moti_b_6927432.

4. Battista, Rebecca A., ed. ACSM's Resources for the Personal Trainer. 5th ed. Philadelphia: Wolters Kluwer, 2018, 200–208.

5. Battista, Rebecca A., ed. ACSM's, 204.

Chapter 10: Safety Every Step of the Way

1. Psalm 91:1–6, 9–12, 14 (NIV).

2. Matthew 19:26 (NIV).

3. 1 Corinthians 10:6 (KJV).

4. Battista, Rebecca A., ed. ACSM's Resources for the Personal

Trainer. 5th ed. Philadelphia: Wolters Kluwer, 2018, 290–292, 299, 304–306, 311.

5. Warburton, Darren E., and Norman Gledhill. "2021 PAR-Q+. The Physical Activity Readiness Questionnaire for Everyone." Accessed January 31, 2022. http://eparmedx.com/wp-content/uploads/2021/01/ParQ-Plus-Jan-2021-Image.pdf.

6. The New PAR-Q+ and ePARmed-X+. "ePARmed-X+." Accessed January 31, 2022. http://eparmedx.com/?page_id=24.

Chapter 11: Facts of Cardiorespiratory Programs

1. Hebrews 12:1–3 (NIV).

2. Battista, Rebecca A., ed. ACSM's Resources for the Personal Trainer. 5th ed. Philadelphia: Wolters Kluwer, 2018, 414–415.

3. Schweiz Z Sportsmed. "The Recommended Quantity and Quality of Exercise for Developing and Maintaining Cardiorespiratory and Muscular Fitness in Healthy Adults. Position Stand of the American College of Sports Medicine." September 1993, 127–137.

4. Haskell, William L., I-Min Lee, Russell R. Pate, Kenneth E. Powell, Steven N. Blair, Barry A. Franklin, Caroline A. Macera, Gregory W. Heath, Paul D. Thompson, Adrian Bauman. "Physical activity and public health: updated recommendation for adults from the American College of Sports Medicine and the American Heart Association." Medicine & Science in Sports & Exercise, August 2007. https://doi.org/10.1249/mss.0b013e3180616b27.

5. Battista, Rebecca A., ed. ACSM's, 417–418; 419–20,436–438.

6. Jeremiah 1:5 (NIV).

Chapter 12: Facts of Resistance Programs

1. 1 Timothy 4:4–9 (KJV).

2. Lifespan Cardiovascular Institute. "Benefits of Resistance Training." Accessed January 31, 2022. https://www.lifespan. org/sites/default/files/lifespan-files/documents/centers/cardio-vascular-institute/benefits-of-resistance-training.pdf.

3. Battista, Rebecca A., ed. ACSM's Resources for the Personal Trainer. 5th ed. Philadelphia: Wolters Kluwer, 2018, 376.

4. Battista, Rebecca A., ed. ACSM's, 362–364.

Chapter 13: Facts of Flexibility Programs

1. Battista, Rebecca A., ed. ACSM's Resources for the Personal Trainer. 5th ed. Philadelphia: Wolters Kluwer, 2018, 354–365.

2. 2 Timothy 2:19–22 (NIV).

3. BBC. "Why are toddlers so flexible?" Accessed January 31, 2022. https://www.bbc.co.uk/tiny-happy-people/amazing-toddlers-bendy-tots/znvvy9q.

4. BetterMe. "What Is The Impact Of Age On Flexibility?" Accessed January 31, 2022. https://betterme.world/articles/what-is-the-impact-of-age-on-flexibility/.

5. Levy, Jillian. "Benefits of Flexibility and How to Become More Flexible." Last modified November 27, 2021. https://

draxe.com/fitness/benefits-of-flexibility/.

Chapter 14: Special Populations

1. Psalm 139:14 (KJV).

2. Matthew 19:26 (NIV).

3. Luke 1:37 (ESV).

4. Battista, Rebecca A., ed. ACSM's Resources for the Personal Trainer. 5th ed. Philadelphia: Wolters Kluwer, 2018, 548–550, 563–565, 551–557.

5. Ding, Karisa. "Postpartum exercise: Is your body ready?" Accessed January 31, 2022. https://www.babycenter.com/baby/postpartum-health/postpartum-exercise-is-your-body-ready_196.

Chapter 15: Designing Your Program

1. 1 Colossians 1:3–6, 9–12 (NIV).

2. Battista, Rebecca A., ed. ACSM's Resources for the Personal Trainer. 5th ed. Philadelphia: Wolters Kluwer, 2018, 358–365.

Chapter 16: The Truth of Good Exercise

1. Luke 11:33–36 (NIV).

2. Beresford, Harry. "How long does it actually take to see results from exercise?" Last modified March 14, 2019. https://exerciseright.com.au/how-long-exercise-results/.

3. Agency for Clinical Innovation. "Cardiovascular System" Accessed January 31, 2022. https://www.aci.health.nsw.gov.au/

networks/icnsw/patients-and-families/patient-conditions/cardiovascular-system.

4. Cleveland Clinic. "Respiratory System." Last modified January 24, 2020. https://my.clevelandclinic.org/health/articles/21205-respiratory-system.

Chapter 17: Breakdown of Nutrition

1. 1 Corinthians 10:23–33 (NIV).

2. Genesis 1:12 (KJV).

3. Genesis 1:29 (KJV).

4. Narins, Elizabeth. "The 21 Craziest Diets Ever—Debunked." Last modified January 21, 2015. https://www.cosmopolitan.com/health-fitness/advice/a35415/craziest-diets-ever-debunked/.

5. Battista, Rebecca A., ed. ACSM's Resources for the Personal Trainer. 5th ed. Philadelphia: Wolters Kluwer, 2018, 164–183.

6. Ecclesiastes 2:24 (KJV).

7. 1 Corinthians 6:12 (KJV).

8. John 15:7 (ESV).

Chapter 18: Combining Faith and Fitness

1. 1 Thessalonians 4:1–12 (NIV).

2. Matthew 5:13–14 (NIV).

ABOUT THE AUTHOR

Josie Kastendieck is the wife of her military husband, Joseph, who serves in the United States Air Force. Before marriage, Josie graduated with a bachelor's in kinesiology: fitness and health in 2018. She shortly became certified as a personal trainer in 2019. Starting in 2021, she started teaching "Healthy Biblical Living" classes at her local church. Josie aspires to teach people the value of healthy living while making God the center of her teaching. She strives to continue speaking at churches to share what God has put on her heart with *Fit to Serve* and desires to use this book as an outreach.

9 781685 565169